Zero Breakdown Strategies

By
Terry Wireman

This book is designed to assist companies, regardless of the type of industry or facility, to develop asset (equipment) management policies which, when properly implemented, will virtually eliminate asset (equipment) malfunctions or breakdowns.

Hanser Gardner Publications
Cincinnati

Library of Congress Cataloging-in-Publication Data

Wireman, Terry.
    Zero breakdown strategies / Terry Wireman.
    p.   cm.
    ISBN 1-56990-259-3
        1. Plant maintenance --Management. 2. Industrial equipment--
    Maintenance and repair.
    I. Title

TS192.W583 1999
658.2'7--dc21

                                                      99-051988

A ***Modern Machine Shop*** book published by
Gardner Publications, Metalworking's Premier Publisher
www.mmsonline.com

Hanser Gardner Publications
6915 Valley Avenue
Cincinnati, OH 45244-3029
www.hansergardner.com

Dedication:

This book is dedicated to my two sons, Justin and Chad
(and eventually their families)

"May they live long and prosper."

Table of Contents:

Chapter 1:
Zero Breakdown Concepts

Introduction to Zero Breakdown Strategies

Are zero breakdowns really achievable at your plant or facility? Is it conceivable—or even desirable—to have zero breakdowns? If we think of quality initiatives, the goal is zero defects. While most companies never achieve this goal, many develop strategies or methodologies that come very close. In fact, six sigma quality is the stated goal for many quality programs.

We can compare maintenance to quality: quality focuses on producing a perfect product; maintenance focuses on providing reliable equipment capable of producing the perfect product. So if zero defects is the goal for quality, should not zero breakdowns be the goal for maintenance? In reality, most companies would never achieve zero breakdowns, so would it be possible to have six sigma reliability? If so, what would be the cost of six sigma reliability? When would the cost of equipment or asset reliability exceed the benefits achieved? How expensive would it really be to achieve zero breakdowns?

These questions can only be answered after clearly defining breakdowns, the business objective of the equipment or asset, and the determination of the steps necessary to achieve zero breakdowns.

Asset Utilization—The Business Objective

Asset utilization, commonly referred to as Overall Equipment Effectiveness, is a complete picture of how equipment or assets perform. It involves examining equipment availability, the equipment performance rate, and the quality rate. The asset utilization may also be referred to as equipment capacity.

Asset utilization is not just the responsibility of one department. It is the

1

responsibility of the entire company. It has the focus of ensuring that nowhere in the world does another company have the same assets or produces greater capacity from those assets. It means being the best at getting the most out of the assets. The measurement of asset utilization is the overall equipment effectiveness. Overall equipment effectiveness is a holistic calculation that measures availability, performance efficiency, and quality rate.

Availability is defined as the percentage of time the equipment is available compared to the time that it is required to be available. Of course, breakdowns, equipment malfunctions, setups and adjustments, and even material shortages, are all possible reasons the equipment may not be available.

Performance rate of the equipment compares the current operating rate of the equipment to the actual design capabilities of the equipment. Many companies use some type of targeted performance, which usually fails to optimize the utilization of the equipment.

Quality rate is the percentage of good product or satisfactory service that the equipment provided compared to what the equipment should have delivered. So defects, rework, off spec product, or unsatisfactory service from the equipment all lower the quality rate.

For equipment to be fully utilized, a blend of all three parameters determines its actual performance. By examining equipment or assets in this manner, companies can avoid a one-dimensional focus on utilization of the asset. In many companies, decisions are made to increase production, which may boost performance rate but lower equipment availability due to a decrease in asset or equipment reliability.

On the other hand, if the maintenance department performs too much maintenance and lowers the availability, then even if the equipment performs as designed, the overall output is lower. This still puts the company in a noncompetitive situation when it comes to asset utilization.

So it is clear that the approach cannot be one dimensional. The true value of measuring the asset utilization in this manner is that it presents a holistic view of the asset or equipment.

Financial Considerations

Currently, most companies are evaluated by financial institutions using indicators such as Return on Net Assets (RONA) or Return on Fixed Assets (ROFA). Equipment or assets that are not performing as designed with maximum availability and acceptable quality will impact these indicators in one or both of the following methods.

1. Lack of asset performance will require excessive investment in redundant equipment, increasing the asset base value and thus impacting the indica-

tors in a negative manner (same profit / higher asset value).

2. The lack of asset performance will reduce the capacity of the equipment, reducing the company's ability to provide its product or service at the design capability of the equipment. This reduction in the output of the equipment will reduce the income generated, thus negatively impacting the indicators (lower profit / same asset value).

The solution to the above problems is to focus on optimizing the utilization of the assets by implementation of strategies to eliminate all equipment breakdowns. In reality, whether a function loss or a function reduction breakdown, all breakdowns impact a company financially. Zero breakdown strategies are designed to provide cost effective solutions to equipment problems that will allow companies to realize the maximum return on investment in their assets.

Major Equipment Losses

In reality, there are six major losses that impact asset utilization:

1. breakdowns
2. setups and adjustments
3. idling and minor stoppages
4. reduced speed or capacity losses
5. quality defects and rework
6. startup and shutdown losses.

When examining the losses closely, we find that some operational equipment experiences losses of product or quality during the startup and shutdown cycles. These losses are referred to as the *startup and shutdown losses*.

Quality losses occur for various reasons. They may be due to an equipment, operational, or even raw material problem.

Reduced speed or capacity losses occur because equipment is not operated at design levels. These losses may be caused by worn equipment, raw material issues, or even operational errors.

Idling and minor stoppage losses are caused by small problems with the equipment. These delays are typically less than five minutes in duration but may occur frequently.

Setups and adjustments, or product and process changeovers, occur when changing equipment to run different products or product mixes. Any unnecessary time spent on these activities is a loss.

Breakdowns seem self-explanatory, however, breakdowns can be far more encompassing than the other losses.

One dictionary defines a breakdown as "the act of failing to function or continue." If this definition is applied to equipment or assets, then anytime the equipment or asset fails to perform when required—at design capacity and with satisfactory quality—it is broken.

Breakdowns

Based on the above definition, all losses are breakdowns. This would also indicate that there are two types of breakdowns: the function loss and function reduction breakdown. Function loss breakdowns occur when all the equipment functioning stops. This is the type of breakdown that most people are familiar with. However, setups and adjustments also stop all equipment functioning. Idling and minor stoppages also stop all equipment functioning even if just for a brief time period. Therefore, any loss that is created when all equipment functioning stops can be considered a function loss breakdown. Of the six major losses, breakdowns, setups and adjustments, and idling and minor stoppage losses would be considered function loss breakdowns.

The second type of breakdown would be a function reduction breakdown. This breakdown is when efficiency losses occur. The equipment may be operating, but it is not achieving design specifications. The analogy would be an automobile in a 60 mph speed zone only achieving 30 mph. In plants or facilities, function reduction losses impact the asset utilization to a point that backup or redundant systems may be utilized. Of the six major losses, idling and minor stoppage losses create function reduction breakdowns. Reduced speed or capacity losses create function reduction breakdowns since efficiency is lost. Quality problems, whether defects or rework, create lost efficiency, so they are considered function reduction breakdowns. Startup and reduced-yield losses also create lost efficiency, and are also considered function reduction breakdowns.

Most companies concentrate on function loss breakdowns, since when the equipment is not functioning, it is quite easy to detect. However, these same companies ignore, or give low priority to solving, function *reduction* breakdowns. Yet, studies have shown that function reduction losses make up the largest part of total overall equipment losses.

In this book, both function loss and function reduction breakdowns are considered. Both types of breakdowns are caused by organizational issues and technical issues. Methodologies to eliminate the losses categorized in the two types of breakdowns will be presented.

Zero breakdown strategies can be categorized into five activities:

1. maintaining basic conditions
2. maintaining operating standards
3. restoring or preventing deterioration
4. improving or eliminating design weaknesses
5. preventing human error.

These will be systematically covered in detail in Section 2.

Regardless of the zero breakdown strategy utilized, the key to being effective is to truly understand the root causes of the breakdown. For example, if a bearing fails, the question "why?" should be asked *five* times. This leads to the root cause of the failure. Consider the following example.

Q. The bearing fails. Why?
A. It was out of lubrication.
Q. Why was it out of lubrication?
A. It was missed on the p.m. inspection.
Q. Why was it missed on the p.m. inspection ?
A. The p.m. did not have enough details, and it was missed.
Q. Why didn't that p.m. have enough detail ?
A. We did not spend enough time developing the p.m.
Q. Why didn't we spend enough time?
A. We didn't have enough resources.

The "five why's" is a simple method of root cause analysis. This method tends to be effective for the majority of analyses that companies need to do on their equipment. While other more advanced types of analyses will be discussed later, the "five why's" will form the basis of a zero breakdown strategy root cause analysis.

Introduction to Zero Breakdown Enablers

There are four major enablers to a zero breakdown initiative. These are areas each company would do well to examine before starting to implement zero breakdown strategies:

1. Preventive Maintenance Program
2. Organizational Structure
3. Skills of the Workforce
4. CMMS or EAM Usage and Support.

Preventive maintenance is the foundation of every successful maintenance program. An effective preventive maintenance program is essential if the goal of zero breakdowns is to be achieved. The primary objective of good preventive maintenance is to prevent interruptions to the equipment operations, thus helping to increase the overall equipment capacity. This can be accomplished by good inspection, cleaning, and servicing, all of which are part of a good preventive maintenance program.

Currently, in the United States, almost 80% of the companies have insufficient or ineffective preventive maintenance programs. A preventive maintenance program is considered effective if less than 20% of all maintenance resources are expended (on a weekly basis) on reactive or unscheduled work activities. There are several major causes of this problem, and it is serious, since the preventive maintenance program forms the foundation for all zero breakdown strategies.

Preventive maintenance endeavors to eliminate the root cause of problems before they can cause any downtime of equipment. One of the most essential parts of any preventive maintenance program is training the correct personnel to develop, implement, and execute the preventive maintenance activities. There are two key people in a preventive maintenance program: the maintenance technician and the planner.

Maintenance Technician and Planner. The technician should be familiar with the equipment and have good craft skills. The familiarity with the equipment enables the technician to know when something is malfunctioning. They should be able to spot most equipment problems before they progress to a point that the equipment breaks down. Their inspection results should be turned in to a planner, who in turn will plan and schedule the repairs necessary when they won't interfere with production or facilities. This could be on a scheduled downturn, a nonoperating turn, or any period when the equipment or asset is not being used. The technician should note on the inspection how long a period of time (in the technician's estimation) that the equipment can continue to run before the repairs must be made. This is important for it gives the planner a time frame to work in. Without this estimation, the planner may wait too long before scheduling the repairs, and the equipment may break down.

Routine Service. In addition to inspections, the planner must schedule routine maintenance service. If any equipment is to remain productive, there must be a routine maintenance program. This routine (or scheduled) program should consist of certain checks and services that should be performed at specific time intervals. It might be compared to the service intervals on an automobile. These services usually fall into five categories: daily, weekly, monthly, semiannually, and annually. The planner must pay attention not only to the quality and detail of the inspections but also the scheduling time frame on these routine items.

Basic routine items and their service intervals are recommended by the manufacturer of the equipment. It's best to follow these recommendations (combined with the technician's recommendations and historical records) when setting routine service intervals. If in doubt, contact the manufacturer; they're very considerate and want their equipment to provide the best service possible. The planner should be someone who is familiar with both the maintenance repair work and also the production/ facilities schedule. This will enable them to best fulfill their assignments. The planner is responsible for maintaining the records for and scheduling the following items:

- inspections of equipment
- routine maintenance of equipment
- repair assignments to the maintenance technicians
- scheduling the followup inspections of the performed work.

It's beneficial if standard forms are provided for the inspections. This makes it easier for all involved. These forms are usually provided by some form of computerized maintenance management system (CMMS). (Additional information on CMMS will be presented later in this section.)

In addition to these scheduling assignments, the planner needs to keep a record of all breakdown repairs. This is commonly referred to as the equipment history and is built from the work order system. This will enable the maintenance supervisor to keep track of all problem areas. If a certain piece of equipment has an abnormal number of breakdowns, the supervisor (in conjunction with the planner) may change some aspect of the routine maintenance performed to eliminate the problem. Detailed inspection of all equipment failures to determine the cause will help eliminate continued breakage of the same component. The technicians can be used to do this type of inspecting. This takes considerable practice, but once the technician becomes proficient at this type of inspection they can save considerable time and money spent on repetitive repairs.

Nondestructive Testing Inspection Techniques. Nondestructive testing and monitoring is another method of inspection that is becoming prevalent in industry. These techniques are usually divided into four basic categories: particle dye, ultrasound, vibration analysis, and oil or lubricant analysis.

Particle dye tests are used to check for defects in equipment. They usually consists of a magnetic dye and a powerful magnet. The dye is spread on the piece of equipment, the magnet is turned on (or placed on the equipment), and the excess is brushed away. Any cracks or defects in the equipment will draw the dye inside. Then some type of light (usually ultraviolet) shows the inspector the location of the cracks or defects. The repair or replacement can then be recommended.

Ultrasound utilizes sonic waves to locate leaks and spot defects in material and equipment components. It may be used to find air leaks, steam leaks, and even some fluid leaks. It is also a useful tool in spotting subsurface defects in equipment without costly disassembly or surprising breakdowns.

Vibration analysis uses a vibration monitor to determine if defects are developing in equipment. The analyzer usually displays waves on a screen according to the type of vibration it senses. By using charts, the inspector can pinpoint what's causing the vibration, and can make recommendations to eliminate the vibration.

Another type of analyzer uses a transmitter with a plug-in meter. The meter gives a numerical output on its display. The technician reads the display, compares it to the chart, and can determine the condition of the particular component. If accurate records are kept, the equipment's gradual deterioration can be charted and a schedule can be set up for replacement of components. This will help prevent unsuspected equipment breakdowns.

Oil or lubricant analysis consists of taking oil samples from drive systems or hydraulic or pneumatic systems, and analyzing them to pinpoint any wear in the system. This can be done by part of the maintenance department or, if the equipment is not available, by an outside company (there are presently several that specialize in this type of testing). This is an effective method of discovering defective components before they fail during production.

All testing equipment is very important to the technician. If they can't spot potential problems during inspections, the maintenance program will not function properly. If good communication is lacking between the technician and the planner, the program will suffer. If the inspections and scheduling are both performed correctly, the benefits will be self-evident.

Preventive maintenance is becoming so important that most industrial plants are investing in computerized systems that help control preventive maintenance activities. These systems are commonly referred to as Computerized Maintenance Management Systems (CMMS). As the systems have evolved and are used as part of an overall company strategy, they are referred to as Enterprise Asset Management Systems (EAM).

Organizational Structure is an overlooked area for organizations attempting to adopt Zero Breakdown Strategies. How a company decides to organize the maintenance function can enable or disable their ability to properly care for the assets/equipment. Organizational design for maintenance includes the following decision points:

- Definition of Maintenance
- Objectives of Maintenance
- Organization and Staffing
- Roles and Responsibilities.

Definition of Maintenance. Maintenance is defined as all actions or activities necessary for keeping a system or equipment component in a desired operational state or restoring it to that state. A maintenance activity may fall into one of the five following categories:

1. Preventive maintenance
2. Corrective maintenance
3. Reactive maintenance
4. Predictive maintenance
5. Maintenance prevention.

Preventive maintenance activities focus on basics. They include proper inspections, proper lubrication, and proper fastening procedures. Preventive maintenance activities should be so effective that at least 80% of all maintenance activities occur on a planned and scheduled basis.

Corrective maintenance activities are generated from preventive maintenance inspections, operational requests, and routine service requirements. These activities should be able to be planned and scheduled at least one week in advance.

Reactive maintenance activities are those that must be performed immediately upon notification. Reactive maintenance activities are responses to equipment breakdowns, especially breakdowns of critical equipment, and situations that do or can lead to production interruptions.

Predictive maintenance activities monitor and trend equipment conditions. This allows proactive replacements of worn or defective components before a failure occurs. A commonly understood difference between preventive and predictive maintenance is that predictive maintenance usually uses a monitoring technology, whereas preventive maintenance is usually more of a manual task.

Maintenance prevention activities focus on changing the design of equipment components so they require less maintenance. Maintenance prevention activities usually are supported by the maintenance engineering group.

Objectives of Maintenance. In order to determine the proper goals and objectives for the maintenance organization, it is first necessary to define its responsibilities. Close examination reveals that the true goal of maintenance is to maintain the capability of the company's assets to perform their designed function.

The second goal of maintenance is to be as efficient and effective as possible in carrying out the repairs and services that are required. By controlling maintenance costs, the maintaining function ensures that no unnecessary expenses are incurred. Keeping costs down maximizes profitability and prevents wasted dollars. However, if the maintenance activities are neither effective nor efficient, it is more economical to contract them out. So, in fact, by being efficient and effective, the maintenance organization ensures the employment of its members.

All five types of maintenance activities must be focused on the objectives of the maintenance organization. While the objectives of maintenance may vary from organization to organization, some typical maintenance objectives are listed below.

1. Maximize production at the lowest cost, the highest quality, and within the optimum safety standards. This statement is very broad, but it is important for maintenance to have a proactive vision to help focus its activities, and this statement should be tied to any corporate objective statements.

2. Identifying and implementing cost reductions is sometimes an overlooked aspect of maintenance. However, there are many ways a maintenance organization can help a company reduce costs. For example, a change in a maintenance policy may lengthen production run times without damaging the equipment. This reduces maintenance cost and, at the same time, increases production capacity.

3. Providing accurate equipment maintenance records allows a company that wishes to track equipment in engineering terms such as *mean time between failure* or *mean time to repair*—and many do—to track this information accurately. Success in this endeavor, however, requires accurate records of each maintenance repair, the duration of the repair, and the run-time between repairs. In larger organizations, this activity produces a tremendous amount of paperwork. That is why most large organizations use some form of a computerized maintenance management system to track this information. But whether a computer is used or not, the information must be accurately tracked. Tracking the data is an important activity for the maintenance department.

4. Collecting necessary maintenance-cost information allows companies to track engineering information such as life-cycle costs. Using life-cycle costing information, companies can purchase assets with the lowest life-cycle costs rather than lowest initial costs. In order to accurately track life-cycle costs, all labor costs, material costs, contracting costs, and other miscellaneous costs must be accurately tracked at the equipment level. Again, to accurately track this information, all equipment-related records must be tracked. This is primarily an activity for the maintenance department.

5. Optimizing maintenance resources includes eliminating waste with effective planning and scheduling techniques. In reactive maintenance organizations, it is estimated that up to one-third of maintenance expenditures are wasted. By optimizing maintenance resources, organizations improve their effectiveness in eliminating this waste. For example, if an organization has a maintenance budget of one million dollars and operates in a reactive mode, it is possible that the organization is wasting over $300,000. When 80–90% of all maintenance activities are planned and scheduled on a weekly basis, there is very little waste to the maintenance process. The goal for a reactive organization is to achieve this level of proficiency.

6. Optimizing capital equipment life means maintaining equipment so that it lasts 30–40% longer than poorly maintained equipment. It is a goal or objective of the maintenance department to keep the equipment properly maintained to achieve the longest life cycle. A preventive maintenance program designed for the life of the equipment is key to obtaining a maximum life cycle. The goal of the maintenance department will then be to perform the correct level of maintenance on the equipment to achieve that maximum life. The focus must be

to perform enough maintenance to achieve this without performing excessive maintenance. One way to determine if there is a problem in this area is to examine new equipment purchases. If equipment purchases are to replace equipment in kind, is it possible that the purchase of the equipment could have been deferred if proper maintenance had been performed on the older equipment? If long life cycles are not being achieved, then the proper level of maintenance is not being performed on the equipment, and the maintenance tasks should be revised.

7. Minimizing energy usage is a natural result of well-maintained equipment. Well-maintained equipment requires 6% (to as much as 11%) less energy to operate than poorly maintained equipment. These percentages were established by international studies, and indicate that it would be beneficial for maintenance organizations to monitor constantly the energy consumption in a plant. Most plants and facilities have equipment that consumes considerable energy if not properly maintained. For example, heat exchangers and coolers that are not cleaned at the proper frequency will consume more energy when heating or cooling. HVAC systems that are not properly maintained will require more energy to provide proper ventilation to a plant or facility. Even small things can have a dramatic impact on energy consumption, e.g., the alignment of couplings in a plant that has a large amount of rotating equipment.

8. Minimizing inventory on hand is another waste-eliminating objective for maintenance organizations. Approximately 50% of a maintenance budget is spent on spare parts and material consumption. In organizations that are reactive, up to 20% of spare parts cost may be waste. When organizations become more planned and controlled, this waste is eliminated. Some typical areas of waste in the inventory and purchasing function include:

- stocking too many spare parts
- expediting spare part delivery
- allowing shelf life to expire
- single line item purchase orders
- vanished spare parts.

So, it is important for the maintenance organization to focus on controlling spare parts and their costs.

While this is not a comprehensive, all-inclusive list, these goals or objectives highlight the impact a proactive maintenance organization can have on a company. Maintenance is more than a "fix it when it breaks" function. Unless the maintenance organization is given or develops a proactive list of goals and objectives, it will always be suboptimized.

Maintenance Evolution

Reactive to **Preventive** to **Operations Involvement** to **Predictive** to **TPM/TPR/EAM**

Companies trying to improve maintenance policies and practices realize, in most cases, that it is an evolutionary process not a revolutionary process. Most organizations began with some form of a reactive maintenance program. Reactive maintenance only repairs equipment when it breaks; there's very little attention paid to the prevention of failure. Rather, the goal is only to repair failures. Organizations in a reactive mode develop a "fix it when it breaks" or "if it isn't broken, don't fix it" mentality. Reactive maintenance is a costly way of doing maintenance. Studies show that organizations using reactive maintenance experience costs two to four times greater than those of a proactive organization. In reactive organizations, the production or operations group is usually not satisfied with the level of service it receives from the maintenance organization. There is constant conflict between the two groups and, in most cases, the maintenance organization loses. This conflict often leads to restructuring, downsizing, changing reporting lines, and excessive contracting out. The key to limiting reactive maintenance is the development of a good preventive maintenance program.

Preventive maintenance activities are designed to prevent equipment from failing. A basic preventive maintenance program includes good inspections, lubrication, and proper fastening techniques. Studies show that as much as 50% of all equipment malfunctions have a root cause in one of these three areas. When an effective preventive maintenance program is developed and implemented, the number of equipment failures are dramatically reduced. Unfortunately, the workload for the maintenance department increases dramatically when all preventive maintenance procedures are correctly developed. Then, the maintenance department often becomes preoccupied with the basic servicing of the equipment and does not have the time to develop higher-level predictive or reliability activities for the equipment. To compensate for the heavy load of preventive maintenance, many companies today look for some form of operations or production involvement to free up some of the maintenance resources to concentrate on higher-level maintenance activities.

Involving operators in performing maintenance on their equipment allows maintenance personnel to concentrate on higher-level maintainability, reliability, and availability activities. The exact activities that the operators might perform, however, vary dramatically from company to company. In some companies, the operators merely fill out work requests and help with some of the maintenance paperwork or computer work. In other companies, operators may actually perform minor maintenance, such as cleaning, inspecting, or servicing of the equipment. The exact level of operations involvement in maintenance activities must be determined for each company individually. Unfortunately, some companies have made the mistake of attempting to use operations involvement to downsize the maintenance organization. When downsizing is the goal, operations involvement usually fails. Operations involvement only succeeds when the focus is on relieving the maintenance people to perform higher level activities.

Predictive maintenance activities are maintenance activities that usually include the introduction of a new level of technology. For example, vibration analysis is typically used on rotating equipment. This technology is useful for determining the wear on components in rotating equipment. By being able to plot and trend this wear, maintenance personnel can then plan and schedule repair or replacement activities with minimal disruption to production or operations. This approach further reduces the amount of production loss, and since the activities are planned and scheduled, it reduces the overall cost of maintenance. Another common predictive tool is thermography. Among other applications, thermography detects heat in electrical connections. The heat is typically generated by a loose connection or a defective component. By determining that there is a problem before the failure occurs, the maintenance department can make the appropriate repair. Oil analysis is a third type of predictive maintenance activity. With oil analysis, two tests can be performed. One test looks at the wear particles in the oil and determines what components in the system are wearing and generating these particles. The second kind of test analyzes the condition of the oil itself to determine whether it needs to be filtered or changed. While these three predictive tools are the most common, there are many other tools available. Maintenance technicians should be the people to decide which predictive tools to use to monitor which pieces of equipment.

In the evolution of maintenance from reactive to predictive, usually only the maintenance and operations groups are involved. However, if the organization is to evolve the maintenance function further, there are other parts of the company that must become involved. For example, consider how purchasing could impact maintenance and operations as they try to maintain equipment. If appropriate spare parts are not kept in stock, unnecessary delays occur when parts are needed but have long lead times. Another way the purchasing department can impact the maintenance and operations groups is in capital equipment procurement. If the purchasing department always purchases equipment from the lowest bidder, the life-cycle costs for the equipment may be higher than necessary. Low-bid purchasing can fail to address proper operational and maintenance concerns during the plant design stage. But it is not the intention here to single out only the purchasing function within organizations. Functions such as design engineering, project engineering, and even production scheduling can impact the operations and maintenance groups. If the equipment or assets are to be truly optimized, then all functions within a company that in some way affect the equipment must be involved in taking a proper maintenance focus.

This total organizational focus can have different names in different companies. For example, the following are some of the common terms used to describe an equipment-centered focus:

Total Productive Maintenance
Total Productive Manufacturing
Total Process Reliability
Enterprise Asset Management.

It is not what an equipment-centered program is called but rather the results sought that must be its focus. When the total organization focuses on optimizing its assets, then the organization can truly become a world-class competitor. However, this improvement evolution takes time. A company does not progress from being reactive to being world-class in a few short days. In fact, companies that have made the transition from reactive to world-class say that it is a three- to five-year journey, and the journey doesn't end there. The real focus is continuous improvement.

Organization and Staffing

In this age of downsizing, organization and staffing are among the most critical issues affecting maintenance and its ability to contribute to Zero Breakdown Strategies. How is the maintenance organization properly staffed? While companies have tried many different staffing formulas over the years, the only perennially successful one is to staff the maintenance department based on work backlog. A maintenance work backlog is the amount of work currently identified as needing to be performed by the maintenance department. This amount of work is measured in hours. Many have tried to measure backlog by the number of work orders, percentage of production hours, etc., but it never works. The only true measure of backlog is based on hours of work to be done. To calculate the backlog, in addition to knowing the hours of maintenance work needed, it is also necessary to understand current workforce capacity. The formula for calculating backlog is as follows:

Backlog = identified work in hours ÷ craft capacity per week (in hours).

For example, a backlog contains 2,800 hours of work that is currently identified. The current workforce is ten technicians who each work 40 hours per week plus 8 hours of overtime per week. Total hours worked per week by the technicians is, then, 480 hours. The company also uses two outside contractors for 40 hours each per week—another 80 hours. So the total capacity for the workforce is 560 hours. If the 2,800 hours in the backlog is divided by the 560 hours of capacity, this produces a backlog of five weeks. An optimum backlog is considered to be between two and four weeks of work. So, at first glance, the five-week backlog does not seem to be too far from the optimum.

If, however, an organization scheduled 560 hours of work from the backlog for their crews next week, it would be virtually impossible to accomplish that 560 hours of planned work. The reason is the amount of emergency or reactive work that occurs on a weekly basis. In some companies, emergency and reactive work makes up as much as 50% of the maintenance department's work-allocation each week. If this is the case, then only 280 hours of additional work can be done. In addition, there are routine assignments—lube routes, rebuilds, and other routine activities. Also, there are meetings, absenteeism, vacations, and training. When all of these factors are considered, the actual hours available to be scheduled might be about 200. If only 200 hours are available to be scheduled, then the backlog is actually 14 weeks. This, of course, is unacceptable. One can only imagine the reaction of the production department when it submits a work order that it expects to be done within two to four weeks, and is told it may take as long as three-and-a-half months to complete the work.

While this scenario is bleak, there is a second, more important problem: the proper identification of work that needs to be performed by the maintenance organization. The maintenance department is staffed based on identified, not actual, work. For example, if someone performed an equipment walk down throughout your entire plant today, how much work that needs to be done, but is not recorded, could be identified? There may be hundreds, if not thousands, of hours of work that need to be performed and are not recorded. This leads to underestimating the backlog and, ultimately, to insufficient staffing of the maintenance department. The organization would revert to a reactive condition, since current staff can never accomplish the required work in a proactive mode.

The goal, then, is to maintain the backlog in the two- to four-week range. If the backlog begins to increase or trend above four weeks, then more resources should be added. From the formula, one can see that there are three options for resources. A company can contract out more work, its employees can work more overtime, or it can hire more employees. Conversely, if the backlog begins to trend or drop below two weeks, the company needs to reduce resources. The company could reduce the amount of outside contract work, reduce the amount of craft overtime, or ultimately reduce the size of the maintenance workforce. If the backlog is calculated weekly and tracked annually, seasonal trends and other spikes can be clearly seen. By reviewing these types of records, a manager can ensure that the department is properly staffed.

Roles and Responsibilities. In order for maintenance organizations to be effective, certain roles and responsibilities must be defined and assigned. While it is beyond the scope of this material to consider all possibilities, the following are general guidelines that can be used. While an organization may not use each of the individual job titles listed in the following section, each of the task lines must be assigned. So, while an organization may not have a front-line maintenance foreman or supervisor who has a responsibility for each individual line item, the line-item task descriptions are essential if maintenance is to be managed and, ultimately, the company's assets cared for.

Maintenance foreman. Tasks that are typically the responsibility of a front-line maintenance foreman or supervisor include the following.

1. Direct the maintenance workforce and provide on-site expertise. When maintenance craft workers are working on an assignment and have questions or need clarification about how to perform a task, the maintenance foreman should be able to provide the guidance. The maintenance foreman is also responsible for making individual job assignments and tracking the progress of individual craft assignments.

2. Ensure that work is accomplished in a safe and efficient manner. The maintenance foreman is also responsible for seeing that each craft worker for whom he or she has responsibility works safely and is provided the information, tools, and direction to work efficiently.

It is a responsibility of the maintenance foreman to manage the maintenance craft workers at least six hours per day, with no more than two hours per day spent on paperwork or meetings. This is known as the 6/2 rule. It is not cost-effective to have the maintenance foreman performing clerical paperwork as the major part of his or her work.

Again, it is not the purpose of this text to determine organizational structures for every company. However, roles must be assigned and performed if maintenance is to be properly supervised. The question each organization must ask is: who has the responsibility for supervising the maintenance function?

Maintenance planner. Another individual in a maintenance organization is the maintenance planner. The maintenance planner is different from a supervisor or foreman. While the supervisor manages the maintenance craft workers, the planner provides logistic support to them.

This highlights the typical responsibilities of a planner. Again, if the organization does not have planners, then who is responsible for all of the logistics coordination? If maintenance is to be performed economically and efficiently, good planning and scheduling is essential. In many organizations, a common mistake is to make the maintenance foreman supervise and plan. However, when a maintenance supervisor has a full load—typically 8 to 12 craft workers—that supervisor will not be able to properly supervise and plan. Since a foreman or supervisor cannot do both jobs correctly, maintenance will not be performed as efficiently and effectively as it could be.

Up to this point, the focus has been on managing the maintenance workforce and providing the support needed to make them efficient and effective. However, now the transition is made to managing assets or equipment. If the first two task lists are properly assigned and completed, then the organization is collecting data through the work order system and the CMMS. The next job description entails making these data focus on achieving zero breakdowns.

Maintenance engineer. In brief, the maintenance engineer is responsible for properly managing assets. The engineer is a key individual if a company is going to maximize asset utilization. A maintenance engineer is different from a project engineer. A project engineer concentrates on new construction and new equipment. The maintenance engineer concentrates on optimizing existing equipment or assets. Ultimately, it is the maintenance engineer's goal to ensure that no organization that has the same kinds of assets as his company gets more production from their assets than his company does. This person provides the technical focus and support that is required to achieve zero breakdowns.

Skills of the Workforce

Technical training and the resulting skill levels in maintenance comprise one of the largest weakness of the present maintenance structure in the majority of companies. It has been estimated that a company should spend approximately $1,200 per year for training of maintenance supervisors, and should spend approximately $1,000 per year for each technician. In fact, if you don't provide some training for a technician in an 18-month time period, his skills become dated. When was the last formal training program for your technicians? For your supervisors? For your planners? The importance of training cannot be overstated.

Without good quality training programs, a maintenance organization will never be cost-effective.

Craft technician training programs. The first level of training must be the technician apprentice training program. This level of training takes the "man on the street" and gives him the training necessary to become a skilled technician. The training program must be a combination of on-the-job training coupled with classroom training. Most good programs will be three to four years in length, with hands-on lab sessions used with the classroom settings.

Some companies work with local vocational schools to fill entry-level craft technician positions. This allows the company to specify some of the material that must be covered in the program. The vocational school benefits because of the assistance in placing the students when they complete the program. Another option is university level training, but this is generally used for more advanced training, later in a craft technician's career.

Journeyman training. Journeyman training is usually related to specific tasks or equipment maintenance procedures. Journeyman training courses can be conducted by in-house experts, vendor specialists, or outside consultants. The training may address a new technology, new equipment, or even a refresher course in basic skills.

Cross-training or pay for knowledge. This subject is included in the training section, since it is becoming increasingly common in progressive organizations. It is a sensitive subject, since it generally involves crossing craft or organizational boundaries. This type of program is essential if maintenance efficiencies and costs are going to be brought in line with the costs incurred by aggressive competition.

The cost savings and other benefits are found in planning and scheduling the maintenance activities. For example, consider a pump motor change out. In a strict craft line environment, it would require:

1. a pipe fitter to disconnect the piping,
2. an electrician to unwire the motor,
3. a millwright to remove the motor, and
4. a utility person to move the motor to the repair area.

The installation would proceed as follows:

1. a utility person to bring the motor to the job area,
2. a millwright to install the motor,
3. an electrician to wire the motor,
4. a machinist to align the motor, and
5. a pipe fitter to connect the piping.

As can be seen, not only are many people involved, but the coordination to ensure that all crafts are available when needed without delay will become extremely difficult. In a "multiskilled" or "cross-trained" environment, there would be one or possibly two technicians sent to the job to complete all the job tasks. The advantages of reduced costs and better coordination are obvious.

The coordination (or lack of) would contribute to higher than necessary maintenance costs, but this is only the start. The resulting delay in repairing or servicing the equipment will result in lost capacity to the equipment for the time period. This cost will be the driver for making the change to a multiskilled environment.

Training is important to all levels of the maintenance organization. Unfortunately, in a volatile financial environment, maintenance programs are the first to be cut back. This is especially true of programs that are perceived by management as nonessential, which includes (in most organizations) training. This short-sighted philosophy must change if maintenance is to be able to fully contribute in a zero breakdown initiative.

CMMS or EAM Usage and Support

Computerized maintenance management systems are tools that help facilitate the management of maintenance and equipment for a company. That is, the goal in implementing a CMMS is to install a tool to better manage maintenance and the company's assets.

To help ensure that the goal is clear, let's review the flow of maintenance information and compare it to a CMMS. The figure below shows a flow diagram for a typical maintenance-information system. As the diagram shows, the goal is to post information against a piece of equipment; that information is eventually stored in the equipment history. It is from this equipment history file that the data are typically derived to analyze items such as the equipment's life-cycle costs, mean-time-between-failures, and mean-time-to-repair. The data to do this analysis are collected against a work order which is written against a piece of equipment. The work order becomes the vehicle to collect the information from various sources.

For example, all labor for work performed on a piece of equipment must be charged to a work order. All spare parts used to repair a piece of equipment must be charged to a work order. The cost of these spare parts is usually provided to the store room from the purchasing department. Any rebuilt spare parts used to repair a piece of equipment must be charged to a work order. Any work that a contractor performs on a piece of equipment must be charged to a work order. Preventive maintenance tasks are usually written as a work order and charged against a piece of equipment. Even predictive maintenance systems that collect information, usually through the preventive maintenance program, are tied to work orders to collect repair costs, labor costs, and material costs against a piece of equipment through the work order system. It is clear, then, that all information must be collected by the work order against a piece of equipment and charged to the history.

It is this information flow that maintenance uses to capture equipment data. These data are computerized when one implements and uses a CMMS. It is beneficial to understand this basic flow when considering a CMMS. If this flow diagram is clearly understood, the need for a CMMS in a zero breakdown initiative is clear.

If the true root cause of problems on company assets/equipment is to be determined, complete and accurate data are required to be input into the CMMS. However, this is not being given the proper level of attention in most companies today.

Maintenance Management System

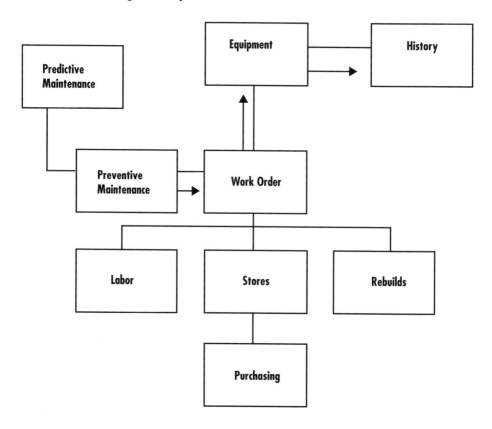

Consider for a moment the work order module of a CMMS. The work order module allows for different types of work orders to be initiated and tracked to completion with the costing and repair information being charged to the correct piece of equipment or facility location. The use of the work order module requires information from all other modules of the CMMS. Some of the information required on a work order includes:

1. the equipment or facility location where the work is being performed
2. the labor requirements (personnel)
3. the parts requirements (inventory)
4. the priority of the work
5. the date the work is needed by (not ASAP)
6. contractor information
7. detailed instructions.

Without accurate information, the work order module cannot collect the required data. Without accurate and complete data, the work order module cannot post accurate information to equipment history. Without accurate data in the equipment history, the organization cannot make timely and cost-effective decisions.

The importance of data collection and analysis to the corporation is highlighted by the following:

- to manage, you must have controls
- to have control, you must measure
- to measure, you must have reporting
- to have reporting, you must collect data.

The timeliness and accuracy of the data collected by a CMMS and the use of the data by the company determine success or failure for the zero breakdown initiative.

As highlighted previously, a CMMS is designed to provide a completely integrated data collection system. However, even among mature users, many are not getting complete (and thus accurate) data from their CMMS. In a survey, respondents were asked about their use of the various modules of their CMMS. One set of responses showed that the majority of the respondents are using less than 70% of their systems. A second question broke this into modules with the following results:

Inventory —52% use the CMMS inventory module
Purchasing—32% use the CMMS purchasing module
Personnel—35% use the CMMS personnel module.

Since the CMMS modules are not being used for these functions, what *is* being used? Some companies are using other corporate systems to deal with these functions, but more than 25% of the respondents are not using any method to collect this information. Even when other corporate systems are used, are the data being accurately posted in the equipment history? In the majority of the cases, the posted data are not accurate (or not even posted), so the equipment history is incomplete or inaccurate.

Some companies have set the CMMS information flow so that the material costs or labor costs are not shown on the work order or equipment history. Any decisions they make will be based on inaccurate or incomplete data, and there will be mistakes. The financial implications of these decisions could spell disaster for a company by placing the company in a condition where it cannot compete with a company making full use of a CMMS and obtaining the subsequent cost benefits.

The solution to CMMS installations, where the data are not being properly collected, is to reevaluate the current use of the system. What data are being collected accurately? What data are incomplete or missing? What parts of the CMMS are being used incorrectly or not at all?

Evaluating the answers to these questions and then working to provide accurate data collection will make CMMS use beneficial to the bottom line. In the competitive marketplace, in which every company currently finds itself, it is unacceptable to make guesses about when data can be provided. The cost benefits obtained by making correct decisions will help to make a company more competitive. Wrong decisions could put a company out of business by taking them out of a competitive position.

Since management requires measurement, and measurement requires data, each company must fully use its CMMS to obtain required data. Without data, a decision is only someone's opinion. Discussions require factual data. Arguments occur when emotions and opinions are involved.

Summary

This chapter pointed out the scope of Zero Breakdown Strategies. It began with the true definition of a "breakdown" and showed that substandard performance cannot be tolerated from any company asset. It also dealt with the enablers required to support Zero Breakdown Strategies. It concluded with information concerning the criticality of good CMMS usage and the need for complete and accurate equipment maintenance data.

Section 1:
Equipment Component Fundamentals

This section is designed to review the basics of equipment component functions. The information presented is critical to Zero Breakdown Strategies. The material reviews the basic function of each major type of mechanical and fluid power system component.

While this material may be a review to many maintenance technicians, studies suggest that the basics are being overlooked or even neglected in most companies today. The material in Chapters 2–12 build the foundation for the concepts presented in the individual strategies in Chapters 13–19.

This section can also be utilized to train new technician apprentices to appreciate the importance of the basics in maintenance, as well as a refresher for the more experienced maintenance technicians.

Chapter 2:
Lubrication Fundamentals

Lubrication Objectives

Lubrication is fundamental to proper equipment maintenance. Lubricants are used for the following purposes:

1. to reduce friction,
2. to reduce metal to metal contact, which reduces wear,
3. to provide a metal-separating wedge of lubricant, which dampens shock loads,
4. to dissipate heat,
5. to prevent rust and corrosion, and
6. to provide a barrier against contamination.

Lubricant Application Methods

Lubricants are applied in the following ways.

1. *Gravity or drip* (Fig. 2–1). The lubricant is fed into the lube system by gravitational force, and usually dispensed in small amounts at slower operating speeds.

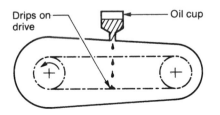

Figure 2-1.
Gravity or drip method
of applying lubricant.

2. *Splash method* (Fig. 2–2). A slinger or some other device splashes the oil onto the part to be lubricated. The oil level must cover the lower part of the slinger to ensure proper amounts of lubricant are being dispersed.

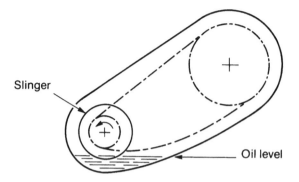

Figure 2-2.   Splash method of applying lubricant. Oil is picked out and splashed on drive. *(Courtesy of P.T. C nents, Inc.)*

3. *Bath method* (Fig. 2–3). The device is partially immersed in oil and the lubricant is carried throughout the system. The oil level must contact the moving parts, since there is no slinger mechanism, as in the splash method.

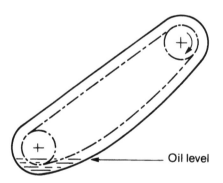

Figure 2-3.   Bath method of applying lubricant. Drive is partially submerged in oil. *(Courtesy of P.T. Components, Inc.)*

4. *Pressure method* (Fig. 2–4). This method is used to spray lubricant in critical areas needing lubrication. Usually a pump dispenses the lubricant. This method is more likely to be used in higher speed applications.

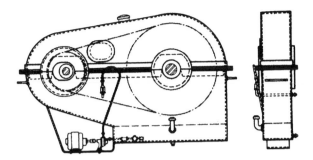

Figure 2-4.   Spray method of applying lubricant. *(Courtesy of P.T. Components, Inc.)*

5. *Manual method.* The lubricant is periodically applied by a brush or some other hand application method. This is usually for slow speed applications.

Types of Lubricants

Lubricants come in divisions based on type. The divisions are as follows:

- liquid—oils of all types
- semisolid—all types of greases
- solid—metals of all types
- gases—used to separate or cool moving surfaces.

Understanding lubrication involves understanding the manufacturer's description of the product. The following is a list of common manufacturer's terms.

1. *Additive.* Any substance added to a lubricant to enhance some particular characteristic. Table 2–1 lists some common additives.
2. *Bleeding.* Separation of oil from its base in grease.
3. *Penetration.* A test for greases. A cone is dropped from a given height into the grease. The depth the cone penetrates is the penetration or consistency rating of the grease.
4. *Dropping point.* The temperature at which a grease becomes a liquid.
5. *Flash point.* The temperature at which a vapor collected from a fluid will ignite.
6. *Neutralization number.* Measure of the acidity of a lubricant.
7. *Oxidation.* Breakdown of lubricant due to heat and air.
8. *Pour point.* The lowest temperature at which a fluid will flow under its own weight.
9. *Pumpability.* The measure of a grease's ability to be pumped.
10. *Viscosity.* A fluid's resistance to flow.

Oils are the most common kind of lubricant. Oils are classified into three categories: mineral oil, animal and vegetable oils, and synthetic lubricants.

Mineral oils are drawn from the ground in the form of crude petroleum. The oils are refined and then the necessary additives are mixed in to provide the qualities that the manufacturer is trying to achieve. These additives will be considered later.

Animal and vegetable oils are derived from natural sources. Animal oils usually come from animal fatty tissues as well as fish oils.

Synthetic lubricants are made from special chemical compounds for use in specific applications where other oils cannot be used. The obvious problem with synthetic lubricants is that they're very expensive to manufacture, but they become useful at high temperatures. Any temperature over 200°F begins to break down animal- or petroleum-based oils. Synthetic lubricants then become a necessity, even at a high cost.

Greases

Greases are usually classified by the type of soap base used in forming the grease. The common types are lithium, sodium, calcium, and aluminum.

Each of the greases has its own qualities, which makes choosing the correct grease a challenge. One caution in selecting greases is to not select a grease that is too heavy because it will channel. This means that it won't flow back into the area that needs lubricating. Also, keep in mind that grease that is too thin won't keep the parts to be lubricated separated, and will allow metal-to-metal contact. This usually results in rapid wear and destruction.

Other Lubricants

Solid lubricants are metals that are soft and have a very low coefficient of friction when in contact with the materials to be lubricated.

Gases are used as lubricants in areas where the materials are constructed so as to allow a cushion of air to separate the moving parts. Some bearings using this principle are called *gastatic* bearings. The caution here is that all gases used as lubricants must be extremely clean.

Many oils and greases couldn't be used in certain applications if the manufacturer didn't blend in some type of additive. Additives are used to give the lubricants certain qualities that are useful in lubrication. Some of the more common additives are listed in Table 2–1.

Additive	Purpose
Oxidation inhibitor	Prevents corrosion and the formation of varnish and sludge.
Detergent	Reduces or prevents the formation of solids.
Dispersant	Keeps deposits in suspension to prevent them from forming on any metal parts.
Extreme pressure	Reduces wear by increasing the film strength of the lubricant.
Foam inhibitor	Prevents the formation of foam.
Pour point depressant	Allows lubricants to pour at lower temperatures.
Viscosity index improver	Improves the viscosity of the lubricant to prevent breakdown at increased temperatures.
Rust preventative	Prevents the formation of rust during equipment shutdowns.
Water repellent	Usually found in greases to prevent the penetration of water into areas needing lubrication.

Table 2-1.   Lubricant Additives

Methods for Applying Lubricants

Greases are usually applied by a hand gun, power gun, or automatic lubricating system.

Hand guns (Fig. 2–5) are usually filled from a large container of lubricant. It may be a bucket or barrel of grease. If it's filled from either of these, care must be taken that the grease is clean. If the container isn't covered, dirt will get into the grease from the surrounding environment. Some companies pay the extra expense to use the individual cartridges of grease to ensure that the grease is clean.

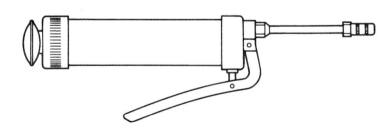

Figure 2-5.   Hand grease gun.

Power guns (Fig. 2–6) are used where larger quantities of grease are required. The gun is usually attached to an air powered pump that provides the grease flow. The danger involved with a power gun is getting too much lubricant. If too much grease is used, it may churn and build up heat and actually damage the equipment it was supposed to lubricate.

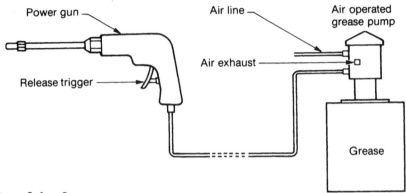

Figure 2-6.   Power grease gun.

Always use the power grease gun in a manner that ensures it will not spray on anyone. Some guns operate at a high pressure. If the grease hits someone at high pressure, it may penetrate the skin. This will usually result in an infection and can cause severe health problems. Safety considerations are always very important.

Automatic lubricating systems (Fig. 2–7) come in a variety of styles and types. The most common has a pump attached to a series of grease lines.

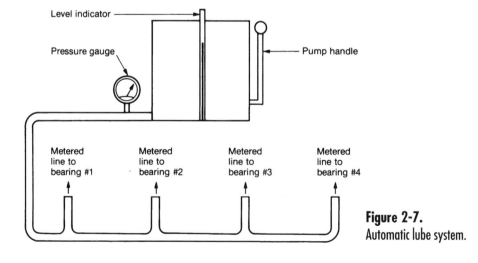

Figure 2-7.
Automatic lube system.

The grease lines are in turn attached to fittings at each lubricating point. As the pump is worked, it dispenses grease in measured quantities to each point. This is a good method for it ensures that each fitting will get grease. It's safer around moving machinery. The technician can stand at a safe location and pump the system without being close to the moving machinery. In addition, most manufacturers offer automated lube systems, with timers and automatic pumps that can eliminate the need for the technician to operate the lube system.

Summary

Lubrication is one of the most important considerations in any mechanical drive system. The lubricant must be chosen carefully and applied judiciously. The basics are outlined in this chapter. For more detailed information, consult one of the lubrication companies.

Chapter 3:
Fastening Fundamentals

A study of the fundamentals important to maintenance technicians wouldn't be complete without looking at screw threads and fastening devices.

Screw Threads

Screw threads are used in all equipment to fasten parts, hold components in position, and to transmit power. The threads may be *internal,* such as a tapped hole or in a nut; or they may be *external*, such as a bolt or a stud. No matter which you may have, they all have terms in common. Following is a list of terms relating to threads.

1. The root of the thread is the base of the thread between two adjacent threads (Fig. 3–1).
2. Major diameter is the term applied to the largest diameter of the thread on a screw or nut.
3. Minor diameter is the smallest diameter of the bolt or nut. This term may be used interchangeably with root diameter (Fig. 3–1).

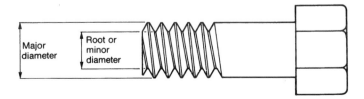

Figure 3-1. Root diameter.

4. Pitch diameter is the major diameter less the minor diameter, divided by two and then added to the minor diameter (Fig. 3-2).
5. Pitch is the distance from one point on a thread to the same point on the next thread, measured axially along the threads.

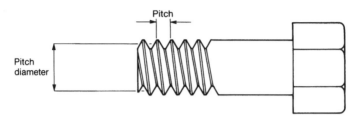

Figure 3-2.   Pitch.

6. Lead is the distance the screw thread moves axially in one full turn. On a single thread, the lead is equal to the pitch. In multiple threads, the lead is equal to the number of thread starts times the pitch. For example, double thread equals 2 times the pitch. (Fig. 3-3)

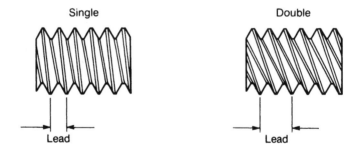

Figure 3-3.   Leads of single and double threads.

7. Multiple threads have more than one starting thread. It's actually like having two or more sets of threads on a fastener. The advantage gained is that you can move a mating nut farther in one turn on a multiple thread than on a single thread without sacrificing the strength of the unit. It'll travel the number of thread starts (2, 3, 4, etc.) times the pitch. These are usually used on units needing faster travel along the threads' axis than can be obtained on a single thread (see Fig. 3-3).
8. Number of threads refers to the number of threads along a 1-inch distance along the threads' axis (Fig. 3–4).

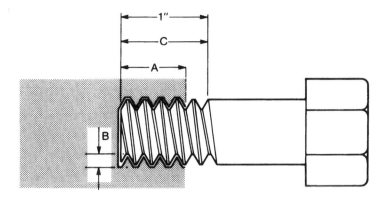

A—Length of engagement.
B—Depth of engagement.
C—Number of threads per inch.

Figure 3-4.   Number of threads.

9. Length of engagement is the length of contact between two mating threaded parts, measured axially.
10. Depth of engagement is the depth of contact between two threaded mating parts, measured radially.
11. Fit is the term used to describe the amount of clearance in mating threads. It has a standard designation as follows:
   1 = loose fit,
   2 = medium fit,
   3 = tight fit,
   A = external threads, and
   B = internal threads.

Fasteners

The most common use of screw threads is in fastening devices such a bolts, studs, and screws. This is the starting point for discussing the correct terminology applied to threaded fasteners.

A *bolt* is used with a *nut* for tightening. If the fastener is threaded into a hole and tightened by turning the head of the fastener, it's called a *screw*.

If it's threaded on both ends, it's called a *stud* (see Fig. 3–5).

The majority of these fasteners use either the Unified National Coarse (UNC) or the Unified National Fine (UNF) thread designations. The vast majority of the threaded fasteners use the UNC designation. The UNF designation is used mainly in automotive and aeronautical work.

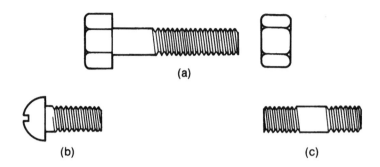

Figure 3-5.   (a) Bolt, (b) screw, (c) stud.

Bolt Grades

There are many materials used to make threaded fasteners, and a detailed description of the metallurgy involved would fill many volumes itself. Let us emphasize the differences by looking at a table of bolt grades (Table 3-1)

Table 3-1		
Grade Marking	**SAE Number**	**Tensile Strength**
	1, 2, 4	60,000 to 115,000 psi
	5	120,000 psi
	7	133,000 psi
	8	150,000 psi

We can see the various strengths of the bolts, but keep in mind that the stronger the bolt, the more expensive it is. Use only the strongest grade you need for the job; not all applications require a grade 8 bolt. If they did, that would be all that's manufactured. The most popular grades of threaded fasteners are the low carbon (grade 2), carbon heat treated (grade 5), and alloy heat treated (grade 8). There's a code for marking the fasteners. The head of the fastener has raised radial lines. The code for the grade of the bolt is the number of lines plus 2. So a grade 5 would have three radial lines on its head. The more radial lines, the greater the strength of the bolt.

Nuts

Nuts are internally threaded fasteners used with bolts, studs, or other externally threaded fasteners.

The *hex nut* (Fig. 3-6) is the most common nut used in fastening applications. The *hex jam nut* is also used in the holding action of fasteners. The hex jam nut is run down against the workpiece, and the standard hex nut is forced against it, effectively locking the threads.

Figure 3-6. Hex nut.

The *hex castle nut* (Fig. 3–7) is used in applications where locking the fastener is important. The nut is equipped with a slot for insertion of a pin to lock the fastener. The bolt or stud must also be drilled for the cotter pin.

Figure 3-7. Hex castle nut.

There are also *square nuts* (Fig. 3–8). They come in standard and heavy series. The heavy series are wider across the flats and also thicker than the standard series. These nuts are usually used with square-headed bolts.

Figure 3-8. Square nut.

Wing nuts (Fig. 3-9) are used when a part is to be assembled and disassembled frequently. The assembly can use only the pressure generated by the fingers. For any assembly requiring more holding force, you should use a standard nut.

The last group of nuts is classified as *lock nuts.* Lock nuts are divided into two categories: prevailing torque and free-spinning. The *prevailing torque* requires torque to run it down the threads. A common type has a synthetic insert that will

Figure 3-9. Wing nut.

resist loosening after the proper torque has been applied. A *free-spinning lock nut* runs on easily, and then deforms under torque—thus the threads are locked.

Washers are also important in fastening applications. They are divided into two classifications: flat washers and lock washers. *Flat washers* are also called bearing washers because they're used to prevent the fastener from cutting into the material it's holding during tightening. They work especially well on soft materials. The styles are too varied to mention, but each manufacturer carries many different styles so consult your local distributor for any unusual applications.

Lock washers are hardened pieces of steel, usually high carbon or alloy steel. The slight deformation in the washer puts extra stress on the nut to prevent loosening. Unfortunately, lock washers are overrated and misused. If the fastener is properly tightened, it doesn't require a lock washer to hold it. The torque applied will deform the threads sufficiently enough to lock the fastener. The problem arises when not enough torque is applied to the fastener to deform the threads; then lock washers are used. If the technician properly torques the fastener, it'll never require a lock washer.

One additional specific fastener that should be considered is *Allen socket head cap screws* (Fig. 3–10). These fasteners are very hard, being rated the same as the grade 8 hex-headed bolt. The fastener must be tightened by a hex wrench. They're used primarily in tool and die work, but are becoming more popular where a strong fastener is required. Allen socket head cap screws come in several different styles.

The *flat headed socket cap screw* (Fig. 3–11) is used when flush mounting of

(a) (b)

Figure 3-10. (a) Allen cap screw, (b) Allen wrench.

an object is important. It may also be used to fasten an object when another object is going to slide on top of it. The head of the bolt being countersunk will prevent any interference.

Figure 3-11.
Flat headed Allen cap screw.

The ***button head socket cap screw*** (Fig. 3-12) is used where a larger bearing area is required for the fastener.

Figure 3-12.   Button head socket cap screw.

Included in the classification of Allen socket headed cap screws is the ***Allen set screw.*** They're usually threaded into a tapped hole for the purpose of fastening or securing two parts together or to prevent movement of mating parts. They come in many different point styles such as cup, (most popular) flat, oval, and cone (Fig. 3–13).

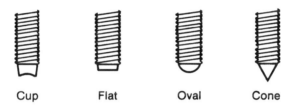

Cup   Flat   Oval   Cone

Figure 3-13.   Button head socket cap screw.

One last point to consider in fasteners is the plastic locking materials such as Loctite® (manufactured by the Loctite Corporation). This is not a commercial endorsement of the product, but it does have its place in mechanical fasteners. When applying the proper grade of locking material correctly, unbelievable holding force can be generated. The important point to remember is to use the lightest grade that will work, and work up to the thicker grades. The good thing is that Loctite is impervious to solvent. The only thing that can break a properly applied bond is heat. It cannot be reused. Once the bond is broken, new material must be applied.

Chapter 4:
Bearing Fundamentals

Introduction

Whenever two moving surfaces are in contact, friction and wear occur. To reduce the amount of friction and thus the amount of wear, bearings were developed. This chapter explores the various types of bearings used in industrial equipment assets today.

Friction occurs in any drive system that has a rotating component resting on a stationary component. The problem is to find a way to reduce the amount of friction. There are two ways to solve this problem: two substances can be utilized that will slide against each other with a minimum of frictional resistance; or a rolling element can be introduced to change the friction from sliding to rolling friction. These two solutions are provided by bearings. The two types are plain or sleeve bearings and rolling element bearings.

Plain or Sleeve Bearings

Plain or sleeve bearings use low-wear materials to support the load. The material usually has a very low coefficient of friction, and is usually coupled with a very good lubricant. The lubricant is used to build a wedge to eliminate any contact between the rotating parts. This may be illustrated by placing two small, flat metal parts on top of each other. As they are moved back and forth, it takes an effort to do so. If the parts are then separated and a film of oil is placed between them, moving them will take less effort when they are put back together. This is the principle of plain bearings.

Plain bearings come in two basic types: hydrostatic and hydrodynamic.

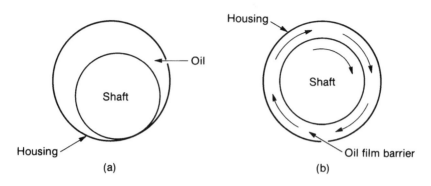

Figure 4-1.   Hydrodynamic sleeve bearing: (a) stationary, (b) rotating.

Hydrodynamic bearings develop the oil film barrier by the rotational velocity of the two rotating parts (Fig. 4–1).

The rotational velocity of the bearing can build lubricant pressures of several hundred pounds per square inch. This pressure will lift the shaft off the inside of the bearing. The same principle applies to a car when the wheels strike a puddle of water and hydroplane. The tire is actually lifted off the pavement by the considerable pressure that is generated. *Hydrostatic bearings* depend on an external source of fluid pressure to provide the separation. They're not designed to develop a metal-separating wedge.

In both classifications of bearings, there are three types of lubricating conditions.

1. *Fluid film.* The surfaces are completely separated by a film of lubricant.
2. *Boundary.* The surfaces are only partially separated by the film of lubricant, and the rest of the load is carried by direct metal to metal contact.
3. *Extreme boundary.* The surfaces are in direct contact on at least the high points or asperities. This may occur when the bearing is deprived of lubrication or under extreme overloads. This results in rapid wear of the bearing (See Fig. 4–2).

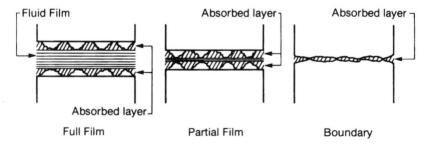

Figure 4-2.   Three types of lubricating conditions.

Sleeve or plain bearings come in a variety of materials. The following is a list of the most common types and their properties.

1. *Babbitt*. This very soft bearing material is used where it is necessary to avoid damage to an expensive shaft. If a failure occurs, the softer material will be destroyed, leaving the shaft virtually undamaged. Using a babbitt bearing has the advantage of allowing a damaged bearing to be scraped in the field and then pouring new metal in the bearing, smoothing the surface, and putting it back into service with a very minimum of downtime. Babbitt is typically utilized for light to moderate loads and operating temperatures under 200°F.

2. *Bronze*. This material is used for heavier loads, slightly higher speeds, and higher temperature ranges (to 300°F) than that used with babbitt. The disadvantage of bronze is that it's a harder material and thus will have a tendency to score the shaft or housing in case of a failure. Also, the bronze sleeve usually can't be repaired. Replacement of the sleeve is required.

3. *Sintered metal*. This material appears sponge-like when conducting a magnified surface examination. The small pores are filled with a lubricant. When rotation begins, the generated heat brings the lubricant out in a capillary action. The problems with this type of bushing are obvious. When the lubricant is depleted, the bearing's life quickly ends. The advantage to this material is that it can be used in locations that are inaccessible for bearings requiring regular lubrication.

4. *Carbon graphite*. This material is used under conditions of extreme temperature (up to 700°F). The carbon graphite type of bushing is the lubricant. As the bushing wears, it lubricates. The factor that dictates when it's time to change the bearing is how much internal play can be tolerated. When the internal motion reaches the stage that it interferes with the operation of the unit, the bearing is replaced with a new one. These sleeves are usually run at light loads and low speeds.

Correct Lubrication of Sleeve Bearings

In the maintenance of sleeve bearings, using the correct lubricant is very important. This means not only the correct amount but also the correct viscosity. The manufacturer's recommendations for each bearing should receive careful consideration. The initial startup temperature should be considered in selecting the lubricant. If a too-high-viscosity lubricant is used in an extremely cold environment, initial scoring, welding, and tearing can occur. This deterioration will continue even if the lubricant reaches its correct operating temperature. If a lubricant is selected with a too-low-viscosity, metal-to-metal contact will result in quick destruction of the bearing. The point here is that in some cases lubricant changes may be seasonal. As the temperature changes, the grade of lubricant utilized may have to be adjusted accordingly.

The filtration of the lubricant is also important. If the lubricant is not filtered, then particles become trapped in the lubricant and are forced into the bearing. Depending on the size of the particle, as it enters the load zone it will scratch or cut the sleeve. The scratches will accelerate the normal wear to an unacceptable level. Careful filtration is a must.

Mounting Procedures

The second important point to consider in maintaining sleeve bearings is the mounting procedure. If too much mounting force is used, the sleeve may be distorted, resulting in insufficient clearance in certain areas of the bearing. This pinched distortion will not allow the sleeve to build up the lubricant wedge, which results in scoring and welding and quickly destroys the sleeve. A second condition that causes the same effect is a housing that's out of round. As the sleeve is pressed into or cramped by the housing, it becomes egg-shaped. When the round shaft is inserted, there's no room for the lubricant to build a wedge, and rapid deterioration occurs.

Rolling Element Bearings

The advantage that rolling element bearings have over sleeve bearings can be illustrated by a book and a table top. When a book is slid over a table, the action is the same as a sleeve bearing (Fig. 4–3).

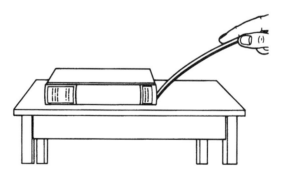

Figure 4-3.   Representation of a sleeve bearing. *(Courtesy of S.K.F. Industries, Inc.)*

When a few pencils are placed under the book, the resulting action is that of a roller bearing (Fig. 4–4).

Finally, when a few balls are placed under the book, the action would be like a ball bearing (Fig. 4–5).

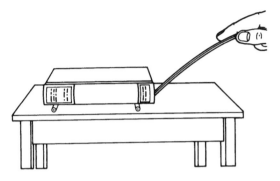

Figure 4-4.   Representation of a roller bearing. *(Courtesy of S.K.F. Industries, Inc.)*

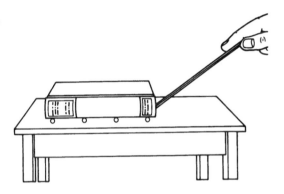

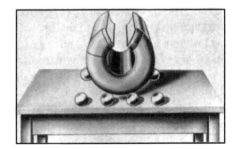

Figure 4-5.   Ball bearing. *(Courtesy of S.K.F. Industries, Inc.)*

In each instance, it takes less and less effort to move the book on the table top. The same is true with the bearings; frictional resistance is diminished as one moves from sleeve to roller to ball bearings.

Ball Bearings

In examining rolling element bearings, the first type to consider is ball bearings. Ball bearing types are best classified by their race configuration. They can be divided in four types: deep groove, self-aligning, angular contact, and thrust.

Deep groove ball bearings (Fig. 4–6) are capable of sustaining both heavy radial and thrust loads. They come in two main configurations, single row and double row. The single row is able to sustain radial and thrust loads. The double row can sustain somewhat heavier radial loads, due to the increased contact area with two rows of balls.

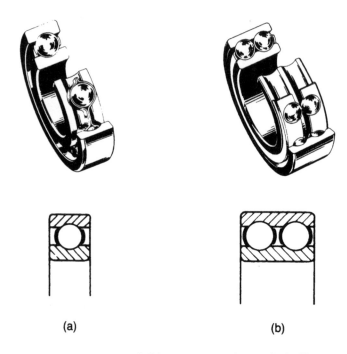

(a)   (b)

Figure 4-6.   Deep groove ball bearings: (a) single row, (b) double row.
(Courtesy of S.K.F. Industries, Inc.)

Deep groove bearings also come in two subtypes, conrad and max (Fig. 4–7). ***Conrad bearings*** have the basic configuration of any deep groove bearing. ***Max bearings*** have loading slots cut into the bearing races. These are cut to allow the manufacturer to insert more balls into the bearing. This enables the max bearing to carry more radial load than the conrad bearing. However, the loading slots restrict the amount of thrust load the max bearing can sustain. If the thrust load forces the balls into the side of the race, they will run across the loading slot. This has the same effect as running your car tire through a large pothole in the

Loading slots

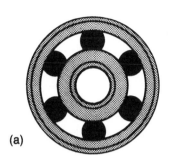
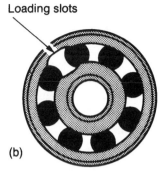

(a)   (b)

Figure 4-7.   (a) Conrad and (b) maximum capacity (max) bearings.
Maximum capacity have more balls.

street. It not only affects the tire (ball) but also the street (race). It'll rapidly remove material through impact loading until failure results.

The maintenance technician should be alert to the type of bearing and its intended load. With this type of bearing (single row, deep groove), it's not possible to install it backward. It is useful to install this type of bearing so that the letter and number codes face outward when mounted. The advantage of this is that the bearing cap or cover can be removed, the number read, and a replacement bearing can be identified and obtained without having to remove the old one.

Self-aligning bearings are another type of ball bearing (Fig. 4–8). This bearing has the advantage of being able to adjust for some slight misalignment. The outer bearing race swivels slightly allowing the bearing to adjust for slight mounting errors, shaft deflections, and base distortions. Another advantage to the curved race is that the bearing race can be pivoted out and the balls and races inspected

Figure 4-8.   Self-aligning ball bearing. *(Courtesy of S.K.F. Industries, Inc.)*

for wear patterns or damage. The disadvantage to this bearing (when compared to the deep groove bearing) is that it can't accommodate much thrust load. The curvature of the outer race doesn't give the balls the necessary support to sustain any thrust loads. These bearings are also available as single and double row, and the amount of radial load should dictate which one is used.

Angular contact bearings, unlike the bearings discussed so far, must not be mounted backwards (Fig. 4–9). The angular contact can take radial loads, but unlike the others, it can take thrust loads in one direction only. Upon examination of the races, it becomes clear as to the reason why. At least one (possibly both, depending on manufacturer) of the races is counterbored. The ball now has a small nest or track to run in. The applied thrust load should try to push the ball into this track. If the load pushes in the other direction it forces the ball to ride on the counterbored shoulder (Fig. 4–10). When this occurs, there is an extremely high loading in a very small area which exceeds the load capability of the bearing steel. The ball or the race will overheat and rupture the oil film

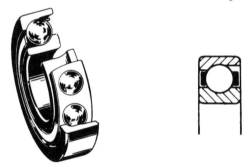

Figure 4-9.   Angular contact ball bearing. *(Courtesy of S.K.F. Industries, Inc.)*

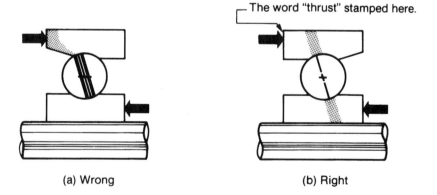

Figure 4-10.   Right and wrong loading on an angular contact ball bearing.
(Courtesy of Fafnir Bearing Div. of Textron Inc.)

barrier, resulting in the welding and tearing of the material in the balls and races. It is important to closely examine the bearing and its intended load before installing the bearing.

The angular contact ball bearing also comes in what is known as a flush-ground type. In flush grinding a bearing, the manufacturer removes material from the inner and outer rings so that when they are mounted, the bearing will be preloaded. Preloading means that some internal clearances are removed from the bearing; this will reduce the amount of free movement or deflection in the bearing. This condition is required when you need bearings that will hold a shaft rigid without any deflection. There are two things to remember when preloading bearings: the higher the speed, the less preload allowed; the slower the speed, the more preload required. Also the more a bearing is preloaded, the more its life is reduced.

The flush grinding of the angular contact bearings factory sets the preload for the set of bearings. This arrangement of mounting is called *duplexing.* Duplexing can be performed in three ways: back to back, face to face, and tandem. Each of the three methods has its own advantage when it comes to mounting. When duplexing bearings, the best procedure is to consult a blueprint for that particular installation. If a blueprint isn't available, then it's advisable to consult bearing distributors for the mounting procedure for the particular installation. Remember that flush ground angular contact ball bearings can be used anywhere that a regular angular contact bearing can be used; however, a standard angular contact bearing cannot be used in a duplex installation. Careful examination must be given anytime an angular contact bearing is being used. The flush ground bearings are plainly identified by each manufacturer on the outside of the box in which the bearing is packaged (Fig. 4–11).

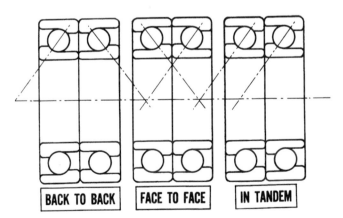

Figure 4-11. Coding and positioning of duplex bearings.
(Courtesy of Fafnir Bearing Div. of Textron Inc.)

The markings are hard to spot on the bearing, because the identification is etched in the race. The other identification is stamped in the race. The etched marking will not show up as well as the stamped, so it requires close inspection to find the markings.

Thrust bearings (Fig. 4–12) are the last class of ball bearings to be considered. They're only used in cases where there are no radial loads. They're not a very common bearing but are found in some specialized installations. The basic configuration looks like a sandwich with two races and the balls in between. Any radial force exerted would cause the bearing to separate.

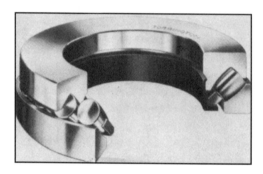

Figure 4-12.   Spherical roller thrust bearing.*(Courtesy of the Torrington Co.)*

Roller Bearings

Ball bearings as a class should be used for higher speeds and lighter loads. If higher loads are encountered, then some form of roller bearing should be considered. However, roller bearings do run at lower speeds than ball bearings. Roller bearings are divided into four main classes by the shape of the roller: spherical, cylindrical, needle, and tapered.

Spherical roller bearings (Fig. 4–13) are the workhorses of this class of bearings. They're capable of sustaining very heavy radial loads and heavy thrust

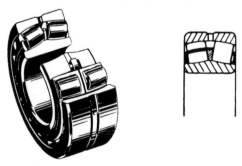

Figure 4-13.   Spherical roller bearing.*(Courtesy of S.K.F. Industries, Inc.)*

loads. Their spherical shape combined with the shape of the outer race gives a large contact area on which the load can be carried. The shape of the outer race also affords it compensation for some misalignment. These bearings may be found in either a single or a double row style, depending on the amount of the load. The shape of the outer race doesn't restrict the amount of thrust load that the bearing can sustain. Although the self-aligning ball bearing couldn't sustain thrust loads, the shape of the rollers allows the spherical bearing to sustain substantial thrust loading. In addition, the spherical roller bearing is designed to sustain heavy radial loads. Some manufacturers design a thrust bearing using the spherical rollers. These bearings are most frequently found in a combination style, where some radial load is also carried.

Cylindrical roller bearings (Fig. 4–14) are the highest speed roller bearings. They're capable of sustaining high radial loads. The bearing can't carry any thrust loads. The design is such that most makes can come apart if radial loads are applied. They may be found in single or double row types depending on the type of service.

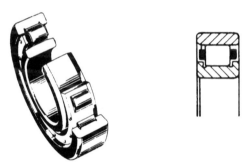

Figure 4-14.   Cylindrical roller bearing.*(Courtesy of S.K.F. Industries, Inc.)*

Needle roller bearings have a roller length of six times its diameter (Fig. 4–15). Needle roller bearings are unique in their design. The bearing has an outer race but no inner race. The shaft that it is mounted on provides the surface that serves as the inner race. At manufacture the outer race is egg shaped. This feature allows a slight preload when the bearing is put in a round housing or is mounted on a round shaft.

One other service note on needle bearings is the difference in the edges of the bearings. The bearing has one end that's hardened and stamped. This is the end that the mounting pressure is to be applied. The other side is spun over or rounded. If the mounting pressure is applied to the rounded edge, the rollers will be pinched or locked up. When the bearing is put in service under these conditions, it'll have flat spots worn on the rollers very quickly. If they're handled properly, needle bearings are very useful in applications with limited space.

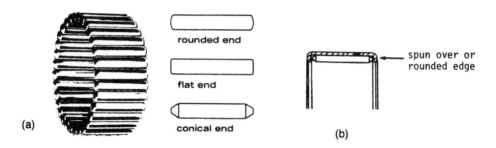

(a)

rounded end

flat end

conical end

(b)

spun over or rounded edge

Figure 4-15. Needle roller bearing. *(a) Courtesy of the Torrington Co. and (b) Courtesy of S.K.F. Industries, Inc.*

Tapered rollers are the last style of roller bearings we will examine (Fig. 4–16). The most common application of this style of bearing is in the wheel bearings on the average automobile. These bearings carry heavy radial loads and heavy thrust loads in one direction only. If there is an application requiring the bearing to take loads in both directions, then two bearings should be mounted opposite each other to take the loads in either direction. This type of bearing will have some type of adjustment, either on the cone or cup, to remove the internal clearances. When the bearing is in operation, it can be adjusted to meet the running requirements.

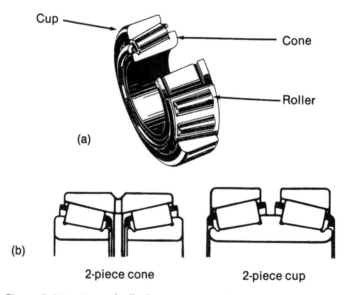

Cup

Cone

Roller

(a)

(b)

2-piece cone

2-piece cup

Figure 4-16. Tapered roller bearings: (a) single roller, (b) double roller. *(Courtesy of S.K.F. Industries, Inc.)*

Preventing Premature Bearing Failure

Between 90 and 95% of all bearings experience what is known as premature failure. This means that they didn't last as long as the manufacturer rated service life (commonly referred to as the L-10 rating). Premature bearing failures can be divided into the following classes: maintenance practices, shaft and housing fits, and lubrication (see Chapter 2).

Maintenance Practices

Many incorrect maintenance procedures are practiced industry-wide because the average technician doesn't know the proper procedures. One of the most common problems is *lack of cleanliness* of the bearings. The oil film wedge that is built in bearings to prevent metal-to-metal contact is from 5 – 30 millionths of an inch thick; the smallest particle of dirt can rupture this film barrier and result in metal-to-metal contact in the bearing. No amount of dirt, no matter how small, can be tolerated in a bearing.

When the manufacturer ships the bearing, it's clean. It comes wrapped in an acid resistant paper that protects the bearing from any outside contamination. The bearing should be kept in the wrapper until it is ready to be used (see Fig. 4–17.) If it is unwrapped and put back in the box without rewrapping, dirt will get in it. When removed and ready for use, it does not need to be washed. The protective slush that is on the bearing is compatible with any petroleum-based lubricants.

 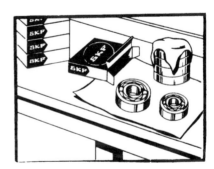

Figure 4-17.   Correct unwrapping of a bearing. *(Courtesy of S.K.F. Industries, Inc.)*

If it is to be used with a synthetic based lubricant, then it will need to be washed. If the bearing is washed, dirt will usually get into it at that time. Most equipment used to wash bearings has been used to wash everything from gears to hand tools. Bearings should not be washed unless absolutely necessary, and then only in clean fluid. Also important when washing bearings is the fluid that you use. A check should be made to see if the solvent leaves a whitish film on the bearing steel. If it does, it should not be used. The deposit that the solvent leaves interferes with the proper lubrication of the bearing steel. Leaded gasolines are particularly noted for leaving this type of deposit. Kerosene is good, but it should all be removed from the bearing before the bearing is installed. One way to do this is to immerse the bearing in warm oil for a short period of time — after washing and before installation.

Anytime a bearing is handled, care should be exercised. If bare, dry, human hands touch the bearing steel, *a* chain reaction begins: the acid in the human body reacts and begins a stain, which becomes an etch, then a pit, and finally a complete rust spot. If this occurs in the running area of the bearing, it'll run rough and fail prematurely. A bearing cannot be started in service with rust on it because the rust will not go away. It will flake off, but when it does part of the bearing will go with it. When the lubricant tries to fill that area, it can't, so at the next load cycle the film barrier will be ruptured and metal-to-metal contact will occur, resulting in continued deterioration of the bearing and complete failure resulting.

No contamination can be tolerated in a bearing. Once in operation, it becomes the function of the lubrication and accessory equipment to keep contamination out of the bearing. Two of the more popular items are seals and shields.

Bearing seals (Fig. 4–18) are usually made of some type of synthetic material that contacts the inner and the outer races. This will prevent the entry of any foreign material into the bearing. The bearing can be equipped with one side sealed, or both sides sealed. If both sides are sealed it becomes quite obvious that relubrication is impossible. Since the bearing cannot be lubricated, its life is limited to the life of the lubricant. This then becomes a factor of the load and speed. Once the lubricant fails, the bearing will quickly follow. If you only have one side sealed, then the bearing can be lubricated through the open side. This allows for extended life of the bearing provided that the lubricant is uncontaminated.

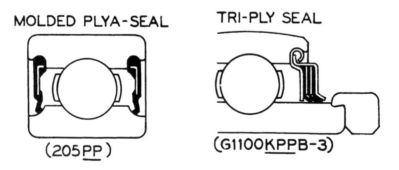

MOLDED PLYA-SEAL   TRI-PLY SEAL

(205 PP)   (G1100KPPB-3)

Figure 4-18.   Bearing seals. *(Courtesy of Fafnir Bearing Div. of Textron Inc.)*

Bearing shields (Fig. 4-19) are inserts in the bearing that are fastened to only one race (usually the outer). There is a very small amount of clearance between it and the other race. The shield won't keep out all contamination as a seal will, but it keeps the larger pieces of dirt, gear chips, metal shavings, etc., out of the bearing. The shield allows lubricant into the bearing, providing extended life.

GREASE SHIELD

(205K<u>DD</u>)

Figure 4-19.   Single shield. *(Courtesy of Fafnir Bearing Div. of Textron Inc.)*

Cleanliness Hints

Any method that's used to eliminate contaminants in a bearing will prevent a premature failure. The following are some basic rules.

1. Always work with bearings with clean tools and in clean surroundings.
2. When removing a bearing from its mounting, clean off all dirt before removing.
3. Always handle with care; do not touch the running areas of the bearing with bare hands.
4. Use clean solvents to wash bearings.
5. Protect clean bearings from all forms of dirt and moisture.
6. If a bearing is to be left for a while, cover it with a clear plastic. If it's to be stored, buy some of the acid resistant bearing paper to wrap the bearing for protection.
7. Always use clean, lint-free rags to wipe or dry bearings.
8. Always use clean lubricants when relubricating a bearing.
9. Always protect the bearings in storage from changes in temperature. The resulting condensation can cause rust to form, ruining the bearing before it's even installed.
10. Never wash a new bearing unless there is some reason to suspect it has become contaminated. The other exception is if a synthetic-based lubricant is to be used.

Item 8 is a particular sore spot to most technicians. If a grease fitting isn't wiped off before a bearing is lubricated, a small speck of dirt that collects on the fitting will be forced into the bearing. This will again cause problems, especially if it's repeated continually over an extended period of time.

The grease or oil may appear to be clean, but if the lubricant sits in an open container for any period of time, dirt will be mixed in the lubricant. Anytime grease is purchased in bulk quantity and grease guns are filled from an open drum, dirt will be present. Although individual grease cartridges are more expensive, they are worth it when you factor in bearing cost.

Bearings in storage should always be protected from temperature changes. Just as coming in from outside (in cold weather) to a warm room will form condensation on eyeglasses, so will exposing bearings to temperature change in storage form condensation on the bearing. The more even the temperature stays while the bearing is in storage, the better condition the bearing will be in when it's ready to be installed.

The handling of the bearing prior to installation will greatly affect the life expectancy of the bearing. If the bearing is dropped, hit with a hammer, or spun with air, it won't last long. If a bearing is considered as fragile as a wristwatch, it wouldn't get as much abuse. Actually, a bearing can have internal tolerances to millionths of an inch—much more precise than most watches. If more bearings were treated with the same care given a good watch, they would last much longer.

Do not air spin bearings. Bearings are not made to run unsupported. If they are, they can explode like a grenade. If it is being held in someone's hands, they will be severely injured, if not killed. It does happen. There are many recorded

Figure 4-20.   Properly air drying a bearing. *(Courtesy of S.K.F. Industries, Inc.)*

instances of individuals who were killed or severely maimed by spinning bearings. It does not matter how slowly a bearing is spun. If the bearing is spun at all, it is usually supported on the fingers. Think of a bearing running without lubrication: it will weld and lock up. If someone is spinning one and it locks up, the bearing will take the fingers that are supporting it off the hand.

One may ask: how will the bearing get dried if air isn't used? The only safe way is to hold both races tightly (Fig. 4–20). This will prevent the bearing from spinning, allowing it to be safely dried.

Shaft and Housing Fits

Another reason for premature bearing failure is incorrect shaft and housing fits. This is probably the most overlooked area in bearing maintenance. Most roller bearings have some method of removing internal clearances; but with ball bearings, this depends on a shaft and a housing of the right size. If the shaft is too large in diameter, then the inner ring must be stretched too far to get it on the shaft (Fig. 4–21). In doing so, any internal clearances in the bearing are reduced, removing the room for the metal separating wedge of lubricant to form, causing metal-to-metal contact and immediate and catastrophic bearing failure. If the shaft is too small, the inner race of the bearing will turn on the shaft causing fretting corrosion, which also causes the bearing to fail prematurely.

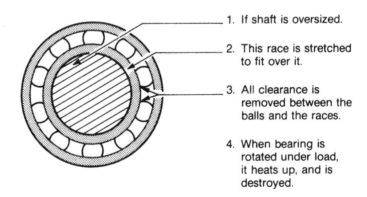

1. If shaft is oversized.

2. This race is stretched to fit over it.

3. All clearance is removed between the balls and the races.

4. When bearing is rotated under load, it heats up, and is destroyed.

Figure 4-21. Oversized shafting.

If the housing is too small (Fig. 4–22), the outer race is compressed, again removing the internal clearances from the bearing causing welding and rapid deterioration. If there is too large a clearance, then the outer race will slip again causing fretting corrosion and rapid deterioration. The only correct way to size shafts and housings is with inside and outside micrometers. The correct sizes

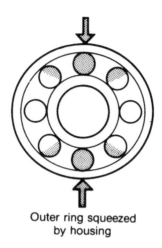

Outer ring squeezed
by housing

Figure 4-22.   A bearing housing that is too small.
(Courtesy of Fafnir Bearing Div. of Textron Inc.)

are found in the manufacturer's specifications for each size bearing. It is critically important to follow their guidelines.

Mounting of Bearings

The mounting of bearings includes more than just having shafts and housings the correct sizes. If the shaft or housing has any nicks or burrs (Fig. 4–23), this sets up additional loads the bearing wasn't designed to take.

The shaft and housing should be smoothed before installing a bearing. Just because the bearing can be forced over the burr doesn't mean that it won't harm

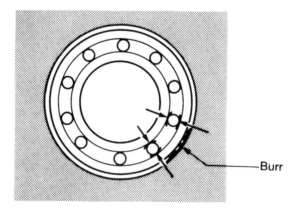

Burr

Figure 4-23.   The effect of a housing burr on a bearing.

the bearing. It will set up stresses that destroy the internal geometry of the bearing.

Mounting bearings can be accomplished by two different procedures: press fitting and temperature mounting.

Press fits (Fig. 4–24) are usually used on bearings less than four inches in diameter.

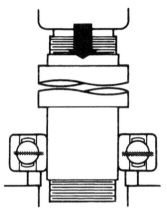

Figure 4-24.   Properly pressing a bearing on a shaft.
(Courtesy of Fafnir Bearing Div. of Textron Inc.)

This is merely a matter of stretching the inner race (or compressing the outer race) till it goes over the shaft (or in the housing). This is the reason it's important to always check the size of all components in an installation.

Temperature mounting is used on larger bearings. It's a matter of using the principle of thermal expansion to enlarge the inner race of the bearing till it slips over the shaft. This is accomplished in an oil bath or by an induction bar (Fig. 6-25).

(a)   *(b)*

Figure 4-25.   (a) Oil bath, (b) induction bar.

An oil bath is merely a tank of oil into which the bearing is submerged, and then heated to the desired temperature. Care must be taken not to overheat the bearing. In most cases, 200°F is sufficient. No bearing should be heated over 300°F. The time and temperature will affect the bearing steel and result in premature failure.

An induction bar is a faster (and a more dangerous) way to heat a bearing. Since it is fast, a bearing can be overheated rapidly. A time chart or heat stick should be used to monitor the temperature. Most double-sealed bearings are heated with an induction bar to prevent any possible damage in the oil bath. These bearings cannot be heated above 200°F. If they are, the lubricant contained inside will be destroyed. In practice, it is best not to heat a double sealed bearing above 180°F to ensure some margin of safety. In temperature mounting a separable-type bearing (a cone and cup tapered roller), it's possible to put the outer race in a freezer to cool it, thus shrinking it, for installation in a housing. Caution must be exercised in removing all condensed moisture before the bearing rollers come in contact with the race.

Never put a whole bearing in a freezer. The moisture that would condense inside the bearing during installation could never be removed. This will cause rust and rapid deterioration of the bearing. Also, never play a cutting or braising torch on a bearing. That's too much heat concentrated in one spot. With no temperature control, the bearing steel will be damaged, shortening the life of the bearing.

Summary

Bearings are the most abused and misused components in mechanical drives. They are mishandled, placed improperly in storage, installed incorrectly, and incorrectly maintained. If the guidelines in this chapter are followed, bearing life would increase dramatically. To do so means to take time to work correctly and carefully. If they're handled as carefully as a wristwatch, they'll provide longer service. Although it's difficult for the technician to make the transition from handling heavy equipment to carefully maintaining bearings, the payoff is not having to change the bearing as frequently, thus reducing unnecessary equipment downtime.

prevent it from drying out, cracking, and breaking. This will also help maintain a good coefficient of friction between the belt and the pulley. Substances such as beef tallow (fat), stearine (a solid fat), or fish oils are used. Mineral oils or waxes won't lubricate a belt or help preserve its coefficient of friction. Rosins will temporarily help but will eventually glaze and destroy the leather surface (also rubber and fabric). If unsure of a dressing, consult the manufacturer for its recommendation.

Rubber belts are made with a tension member, vulcanized between layers of rubber, and are used in outdoor conditions or where conditions don't permit the use of a leather belt.

Canvas belts are used in any conditions, usually where leather or rubber belts can't be used.

Flat Belt Maintenance

There are four basic steps to flat belt maintenance.

1. Keep belts tight. The belts derive their power from the friction between the belt and the pulley. As the tension is increased, the friction increases. The more tension, the more power the belt will have. There's a limit to the amount of tension that a belt can withstand. It will stretch with tension, and once the elastic limit of the belt is reached, more tension will not increase the amount of friction; so it won't transmit more power. If more power is still needed, use a thicker leather belt, since it will have a higher elastic limit.

2. Keep belts clean. If material is allowed to build up on the belts, it will cause a lack of friction. This condition is called glazing. The material can be scraped off by using a piece of angle iron or a block of wood. Always scrape in the direction opposite the joint in the lap of the belt to prevent it from catching on the scraper and damaging the belt.

3. Keep belts properly dressed. Use one of the previously mentioned substances for a dressing or consult the manufacturer for recommendations. Rosins, oils, and waxes are not good dressings. The dressing should keep the belt pliable and maintain the coefficient of friction. Do not use excessive amounts of dressing, since it will reduce the belt's stiffness and allow excessive give in a lateral direction.

4. Protect the belts. High temperature and high humidity can damage a belt. Efforts should be made to keep the belts in a cool and dry environment. All foreign substances should be kept off the belts, such as oil, grease, and dust. The drive should be protected to keep obstacles from falling into the belt or pulley. If an object is between the pulley and the belt, some of the support in the belt will probably be damaged, preventing it from tracking correctly.

Comparison of Flat Belts to V-belts

Flat belts require high tension, which means high bearing loads. V-belts require medium tension, which means less bearing loads. Flat belt drives tolerate no misalignment, while V-belts can tolerate small amounts of misalignment. Neither drive has vibration. Flat belts have some belt slap, while V-belts run with no noise. Flat belts require occasional dressing; V-belts require no dressing. Neither drive requires lubrication, and the initial cost for each drive is approximately the same.

V-Belts derive their ability to transmit power from the contact between the sheave walls and the sides of the belt (Fig. 5-2). V-belts should never run in contact with the bottom of the sheave. The advantages of V-belts over other types of drives are that they:

- permit a large speed ratio
- permit a compact drive design
- cushion the motor and bearings against load changes
- have no vibration or noise
- do not require lubrication
- do not shut down without warning.

There are three main classes of V-belts: the light duty belt, the standard multiple belt, and the wedge belt.

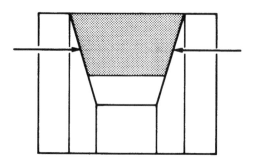

Figure 5-2.   Location of tension areas of belt and pulley.

Light Duty Belts are also referred to as fractional horsepower belts (FHP) (Fig. 5–3). These belts are used for light weight service and low horsepower applications. The cording and envelope of these belts are lightweight, due to the fact that the belts are generally short (10 to 100 inches) and bend over short radius pulleys. The approximate distance across the top of the belt is determined by the number of the belt: 2L ($^{1}/_{4}$ inch across the top of the belt), 3L ($^{3}/_{8}$ inch across the top of the belt), 4L ($^{1}/_{2}$ inch across the top of the belt), 5L

$^{21}/_{32}$ inch across the top). The length code is as follows: 4L 150 belt is a 4L ($^1/_2$) belt, 15.0 inches long, outside length.

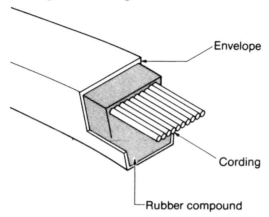

Figure 5-3. Fractional horsepower (FHP) belt.

Standard Multiple Belts (Fig. 5–4) are available in five different cross sectional areas. They are approximately A ($^1/_2$ inch), B ($^{21}/_{32}$ inch), C ($^7/_8$ inch), D (1-$^1/_4$ inch), and E (1-$^1/_2$ inch). The distances given are the widths across the top of the belt. These belts are available in sizes from 25 to 660 inches. They have multiple cord construction for added strength and shock loads. The length code is as follows: A B-70 means a B cross section V-belt with a length of 70 inches.

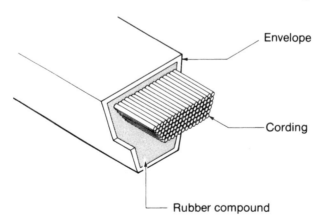

Figure 5-4. Standard multiple belt.

Wedge Belts (Fig. 5–5) are an improved design V-belt. These belts can transmit equal power with a smaller cross sectional area. They use three sizes to replace the five standard sizes: 3V ($^3/_8$ inch across the top), 5V ($^5/_8$ inch across the top), and 8V (1 inch across the top). The belts are run with higher tensions than the standard belts, and usually have to be tensioned with a tensioning tool, which will be discussed later. Lengths on this belt run from 25 inches to 500 inches. The coding system is identical to the FHP belts. For example, 3V 250 means a 3V cross section belt, 25.0 inches long.

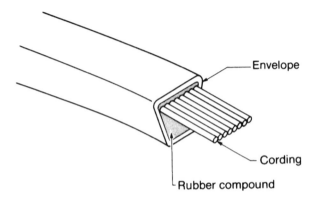

Figure 5-5. Wedge belt.

V-Belt Installation

The first thing to check when installing a set of V-belts is the alignment of the sheaves. There are three types of misalignment that can affect a belt's life: angular (Fig. 5–6a), parallel (Fig. 5–6b), and sheave misalignment (Fig. 5–7).

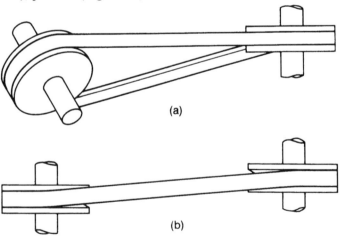

Figure 5-6. Angular (a) and parallel (b) misalignment of belts.

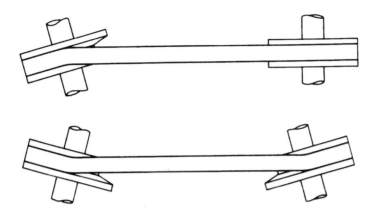

Figure 5-7. Sheave misalignment.

There are ways to check alignment of the pulleys before installing new belts that are convenient for the technician. The first way is to stretch a piece of string across the face of the pulleys, making sure it touches on all four points (Fig. 5–8).

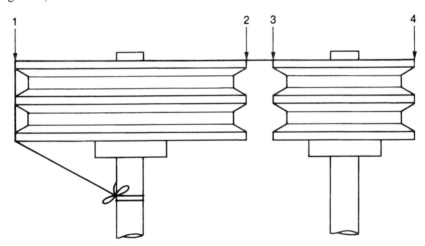

Figure 5-8. Checking pulley alignment.

The second way is to use a piece of string and two squares to make sure the shafts are aligned. The third way is to use a machinist level and measuring bars or steel rule. Follow these steps to install V-belts.

1. Reduce the center-to-center distance of the pulleys. Belts are not to be pried into the sheaves. This will break the tension members (cords) in the belt. The belt will be unable to carry its full load with the cords broken.

This may also cause the belts to turn over in the sheave grooves, or to narrow down in the place where the cords are broken.

2. Keep the belt slack on one side when tightening the belts. This will ensure that all belts will be carrying the same load.

3. Tighten the belts. This step is important because all belts must be properly tensioned for maximum service life. Too much tension puts too great a load on bearings and drive components. Too little tension causes the belts to slip, and thus damages the belts and sheaves.

4. Recheck belt tension after a run-in period of 24–48 hours. This ensures that the initial belt stretch and seating has not left the belt too loose to provide proper load carrying capacity.

After these steps are completed, the belts and sheaves will provide you with the maximum service life. The first three steps will not provide maximum life if step four is not properly carried out. The tensioning of a belt is the hardest step in installing new belts. Most technicians feel that as long as the belt isn't squealing, it's tight enough. This is not true. A V-belt can slip up without squealing. You can lose up to one-fifth of your belt capacity (20%) without realizing it.

Standard multiple and fractional HP belts, when properly tensioned, will have a spring when struck by an object. They'll have a dead feel to them if they're too loose when struck by your hand. If they're too tight, they will feel as if they have no give to them; they will be rigid.

The correct way to tension them is with a belt tensioning tool that may be purchased from any belt distributor. Wedge belts can't be tensioned by hand, because they must be so tight. Most technicians don't give them enough tension. The only correct way to tension a wedge belt is by the use of a tension tool.

Proper maintenance also includes checking the condition of the sheave groove. Worn sheave grooves (Fig. 5–9) will shorten belt life. If the sheave grooves are worn, the belts may bottom out in the grooves. This will allow the belt to slip excessively. The sheaves usually dish out on the sides when worn. When this

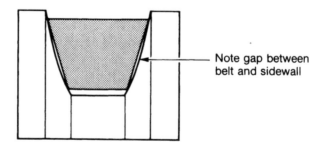

Note gap between belt and sidewall

Figure 5-9.   Installation of a new belt in a worn sheave groove.

happens the sheave will wear the corners of the belt. Continued slippage and eventual destruction of the belt will result. A sheave groove gauge can be used to determine excessive wear (Fig. 5–10). The gauge can be placed in the sheave and a feeler gauge used to measure the wear. If there's excessive clearance, the solution is to replace the sheaves.

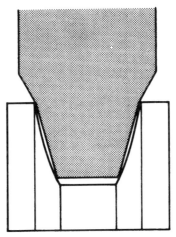

Figure 5-10.   Sheave groove gauge.

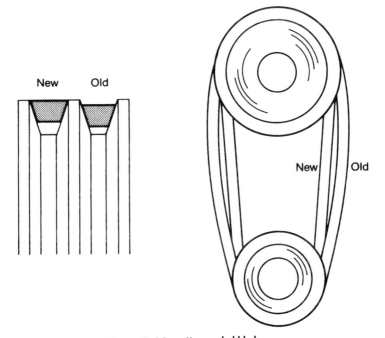

Figure 5-11.   New and old belts.

Replacement Belts

The next point of consideration is the proper replacement belt. When replacing belts on a multiple drive, don't mix old and new belts (Fig. 5–11). The old belt will be elongated, and will be longer than the new replacement belt. The old belt, then, will not carry its share of the load. The new belt will be overloaded and will fail prematurely. All new belts should be checked to be sure that the match code is the same. The code is as follows:

C 40 (manufacturer's name) 50

The C 40 tells you that the belt is a C cross section, standard multiple belt with an outside length of 40 inches. The match code 50 tells you that the belt is 40 inches long. If the code is more than 50 (for example, 51, 52, 53), it's longer than its stated length. The more over its stated length, the higher the match code number. If the number is less than 50, then the belt is shorter than its stated length. The less the number (49, 48, 47, 46, etc.), the more it is shorter than its stated length. The belts should be checked to ensure that they are made by the same manufacturer. The belts, even with the same match code, vary somewhat in length from manufacturer to manufacturer.

As the belts are installed, they should never be pried on the sheaves. Another bad installation practice is to run the belts on the sheave. These methods of installation will damage the internal cords and render the belt unfit for service.

Belt Tension

The next point to consider is the belt tension, for this can dramatically affect belt life. The ideal tension is the lowest tension at which the belt won't slip under peak load conditions. Overtensioning shortens both belt and bearing life. The sheave alignment must be maintained while tensioning the drive. The belts must be kept free from any foreign material which may cause them to slip. Belt tension should be checked frequently during the first 24 – 48 hours of operation. After the initial tensioning period, the belts should be checked on a periodic basis for proper tension.

Guards

The guards should always be replaced to prevent foreign objects from falling into the drive. Guards should be made of screened or meshed material because they allow air to circulate, preventing the buildup of excessive heat.

Idlers

If a drive has an idler, it should be properly adjusted during installation of the belts. A properly designed V-belt drive won't require an idler if proper tension can be maintained. The use of idlers should be avoided, if at all possible. The idler will put an additional bending stress point on the belt, which reduces its service life. The *inside idler* is located on the inside of the belt on the slack side of the drive (Fig. 5–12).

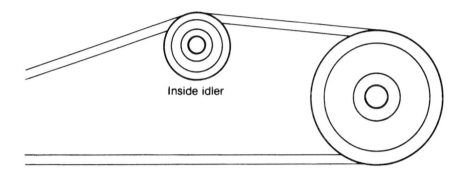

Figure 5-12. Inside idler.

The idler should be located near the large sheave in the drive, to avoid reducing the arc of contact on the small sheave. The size of the idler pulley should be at least equal to or greater than the size of the small sheave. A *backside idler* increases the arc of contact on both sheaves; however, it also forces a back bend in the V-belt that contributes to premature failure (Fig. 5–13). This idler also puts extra stress in the bottom of the belt, which will result in the bottom cracking. It should not be used unless absolutely necessary. If it's used, the pulley should be at least $1^1/_2$ times the size of the small sheave and located as close to the small sheave as possible.

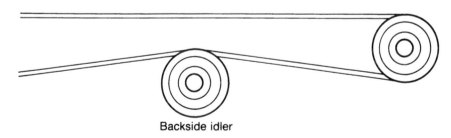

Figure 5-13. Backside idler.

The *kiss idler* differs from either of the other two, since it doesn't affect the belt span (Fig. 5–14). Since it doesn't bend the belt, it won't contribute to premature belt failure. It isn't a common idler, but it's used for controlling vibration and whip on drives with shock and pulsating loads. If this idler is used, the diameter of the pulley should be 1-$^1/_2$ times the diameter of the small sheave.

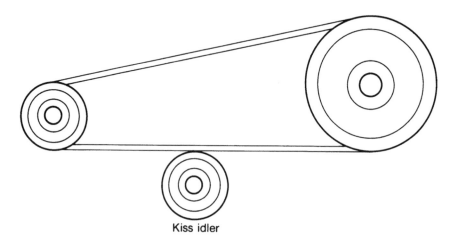

Kiss idler

Figure 5-14.   Kiss idler.

V-Belt Maintenance

Since V-belts are basically a trouble-free drive system, they usually don't receive the minimal care needed to deliver maximum service life. The belt runs until it is destroyed and then a new one is put on and the drive restarted. What if the technician could look at the belt and determine what caused the failure, before installing new belts? This would allow them to correct the problem and then get maximum wear out of the new belts.

Belts exposed to oil and grease will fail prematurely. Any oil or grease leakage on the belts should be prevented. Repairs should be made to stop the leak. If the leak cannot be stopped, special oil-resistant belts should be used.

Another problem could be too little oil and grease in the bearings, resulting in high loads and premature belt failure.

The sheaves should always be checked for free rotation before installing new belts. Dirt and dust will rapidly accelerate belt envelope wear. When the belt enters the sheave, the dust and dirt get between the belt and the wall of the sheave. The belt will then slip due to poor frictional contact with the pulley. The slippage combined with the dirt and dust in the sheave will leave the belt envelope in the same condition as if you rubbed it with sandpaper. The envelope wear will progress until complete belt failure results.

Belt guards are mentioned again here only as a reminder. They should be vented to prevent heat buildup and also should be checked to ensure they're not rubbing the belt. If the guard rubs against the belt, it will damage the envelope and result in premature belt failure.

Belt dressing should never be applied to any V-belt. The system is designed to run without belt dressing. Dressing will only contribute to belt wear and eventual failure.

The cracks that a belt develops in the bottom envelope and rubber won't reduce the tensile strength or the operating efficiency of the belt. The cracks are caused by high temperatures, small diameter pulleys, or a backside idler. It isn't necessary to replace a belt simply because bottom cracking has been observed.

V-belts are cured with a controlled heat for a given time. Belts can operate at a temperature of 140°F or less, without being effected by the heat. At any temperature greater than 140°F, the belts will over cure and not give maximum service life. Environmental conditions should be considered when installing V-belts, for excessive temperatures may indicate the need for special belts.

The following is a description of belt wear and maintenance problems. The probable causes and cures are described.

Rapid belt wear. On a belt drive which shows rapid belt wear, there are several items to check.

1. Check to see if the guard is rubbing the belt.
2. Check to see if the sheaves are worn.
3. Make sure the belts are matched in a multiple belt drive.
4. Check the sheaves for proper alignment.
5. Check the tension to ensure there's no belt slippage.
6. Make sure the drive is free of dust or abrasive contaminants.
7. Make sure the belts are properly installed.

Belts turning over in the sheaves. When the drive is started and run for a short period of time, the belts may have a tendency to turn over in the sheaves. If this condition exists, check the following.

1. Check the drive alignment.
2. Check the tension. If the drive has pulsating loads, the tension may need to be increased.
3. The belts may have broken internal cords. The only correction here is to properly install new belts.

Belts slipping slightly. When the drive is running and you notice the belts slipping slightly, check the following.

1. Proper belt tension.
2. Check to see if the belts are bottoming in the sheave.
3. See if there's oil or grease leaking on the drive.

Excessive belt slippage and belt squeal. When the slippage becomes excessive (over 20%), it will be accompanied by belt squeal. This can be corrected by the same steps in the previous paragraph, with the following exceptions.

1. An overloaded belt drive may require the addition of another belt to the drive, or a higher rated belt.
2. A too-small sheave won't carry the load. Check to see if any recent changes were made in the drive system. The size of the sheave or belt may need to be increased.

Belts breaking. If a belt drive has a continual problem of breaking belts, the following items should be checked.

1. See if the belt drive is subject to shock loads. If so, then the belt tension needs to be increased.
2. Check to see that proper installation procedures are being followed. It's possible the belts are suffering damage during installation.
3. Check to ensure there's no slack in the belt. If there is, apply proper tension. A slack belt subjected to a sudden tension will have incalculable stresses put upon it.

Loose cover or envelope. If a drive is inspected and the belt has a loose cover or envelope, or is swollen, the following should be checked.

1. Is the belt properly ventilated so that the heat buildup isn't excessive? Is it installed in an excessively hot area? If so, provide a method of ventilation or consult the belt distributor for a specially designed belt.
2. The drive should also be checked to ensure that the drive isn't getting oil or grease on the belt. If so, the condition should be corrected, and the belts and sheaves cleaned or replaced.

Hardened or cracked belt. If the underside of the belt becomes hardened or cracked, the following items should be given attention.

1. If the heat is excessive, the belt should be properly ventilated or a special-construction, heat-resistant belt should be used.
2. Belt slippage will also cause excessive frictional heat between the belt and the pulley. This will cause hardening and cracking. Retensioning will cure the problem.
3. The use of a substandard backside idler or a too-small sheave will cause this also. Drive design should be checked.

Stretched belt. If a belt appears to be stretched, consider the following.

1. In the first 24–48 hours of operation, some initial stretch and seating is normal. Readjustment of the tension is required.

2. If the stretch continues to be a problem, the belts will most likely have broken internal cords. Replacing the belts, following proper installation procedures, is recommended.

Narrow spots on belt. If the belt develops narrow spots in it, the following is to be considered.

1. Internal cords are broken due to the shock loads or poor installation practices. Run the belts to destruction and properly install new ones.

Whip. If the belts have considerable amounts of whip, check the following.

1. Check the tension in the belt. If the belt has slack in it, it will have whip. Tension it properly.
2. The center-to-center pulley distances will be too long. Install a kiss idler to dampen the vibration.

If a belt develops a ***chirping sound*** (not unlike a bird), it's nothing serious. Dust is usually the problem. Never try to correct this problem by applying oil or dressing. Realignment of the sheaves and idler may help. Chirping is annoying, but it won't harm the belts.

Toothed or Timing Belts

The timing belts can be used in more types of applications than any other belts or drive systems. They're economical and efficient, and provide superior performance. Timing belts can transmit many hundreds of horsepower and can operate in speed ranges of 0 to over 16,000 fpm (feet per minute). In comparison to other power transmission systems, the timing belt drives have outstanding advantages. They don't rely on friction because of their positive slip-proof engagement (Fig. 5–15).

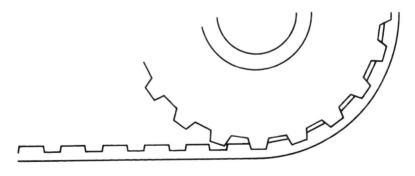

Figure 5-15. Timing belt drive.

They also don't require high tension as do the V-belt and flat belt drives. This produces less loading of the bearings and related drive equipment. Timing belts run free of chatter and vibration. The belts are designed so that there's an extremely small amount of backlash. They frequently outperform gear drives. The fact that they require no lubrication and low tension makes the timing belt drive virtually maintenance free. The teeth of the belt are designed to provide positive engagement with the mating grooves of the pulley. The teeth enter and leave the pulley with a rolling action, with very little friction. The belt teeth function the same as the teeth on a gear. The belts don't rely on thickness to develop their strength. They can be thin to reduce heat buildup without sacrificing strength. The belt construction consists of four parts (see Fig. 5–16).

1. *The tension member*. This is a continuously wound tension member. It has a high tensile strength, excellent flexibility, and resistance to elongation.
2. *The neoprene backing*. The backing and the teeth are made from the same material. They're molded together during the construction of the belt. The flexible neoprene protects the tension members from oil and moisture.
3. *The neoprene teeth*. The teeth are precisely molded and accurately spaced. They are designed so the pitch of the teeth is not changed when the belt is flexed. The tooth shear strength exceeds the strength of the belt when six or more teeth are engaged in the pulley.
4. *The nylon facing*. This is a fabric facing that covers the toothed side of the belt. It's designed as a protection for the toothed surfaces. It normally outlasts the other components of the belt.

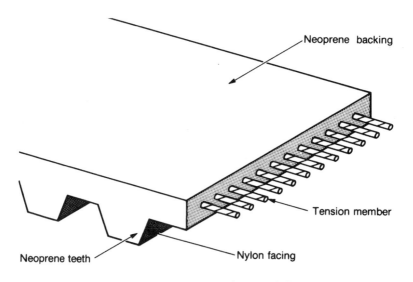

Figure 5-16. Construction of a timing belt.

Most manufacturers produce these belts with five different pitches: X1 = $\frac{1}{5}$ inch, L = $\frac{3}{8}$ inch, H = $\frac{1}{2}$ inch, XH = $\frac{7}{8}$ inch, XXH = 1-$\frac{1}{4}$ inch. The belts will be specified by a code. They appear as follows: 225 L 075. The 225 is the length multiplied by 10 or 22.5 inches. The L is the pitch code (L = $\frac{3}{8}$ inch). The 075 is the width divided by 10; for example, $\frac{3}{4}$ inch = .75 divided by 10 = .075.

Installing Timing Belts

When installing timing belts, proper tension is important. The belt's positive grip eliminates the need for high tension. The belt should be installed with a snug fit. This will produce less wear on the bearings and provide quieter operation. When the belt is installed with excessive tension, it will fail prematurely. If the belt is too loose, it will jump teeth under load, which will shear off the teeth.

The belt should never be pried over the sheave during installation. Reducing the center-to-center distance or the idler tension will permit easy installation. If this cannot be done, remove the pulleys, place the belt on them, then reinstall the pulleys.

Drive misalignment results in unequal tension and belt edge wear. Pulley alignment should be checked to assure that they are parallel. It's also important on long drives to have enough tension on the belt to prevent the tight side teeth and the slack side teeth from coming in contact with one another.

Idlers can be used if necessary with timing belts. The idler should be on the slack side of the belt. It's recommended that the idler pulley be grooved. The idler shouldn't be crowned, and should have flanges to ensure proper belt tracking. The idler diameter should always be larger than the smallest recommended pulley.

Causes and Cures of Timing Belt Problems

Following is a description of common belt wear and maintenance problems. The probable cause and cures are described.

1. *Excessive edge wear*. If the belt experiences excessive edge wear, the following points should be checked.
   - Misalignment. Check to ensure that the pulleys are correctly aligned.
   - Damaged flange. Check to see if the flanges are damaged. If they are, repair or replace them.
2. *Backing problems*. If the belt develops problems with the backing, consider the following points.
   - Environmental temperature. If the temperature is too low, the backing will develop cracks. If the temperature is too high, the back will soften. If the conditions cannot be changed, consult your distributor for a temperature resistant belt.

- Oil or grease. If oil or grease gets on the belt it will soften the neoprene backing. Repair the leak or use an oil resistant belt.
3. *Teeth shearing off.* If the teeth shear off of the belt, consider the following.
   - Is the pulley diameter too small? If there are less than six teeth in mesh, tooth shear can occur.
   - Is the belt load above its rated load? Is there a mechanical bind in the drive resulting in an overload?
4. *Teeth wear.* If the belt wears rapidly on the toothed side of the belt look for the following.
   - Does a drive overload condition exist?
   - Tension. Is there excessive tension on the belt drive?

Ribbed Belts

Ribbed belts are single units with a longitudinally ribbed traction surface (Fig. 5–17). The ribs mate with sheave grooves of the same shape. Ribbed belts combine the fine qualities of both the flat belt and the V-belt. Ribbed belts have a greater area of belt and sheave groove contact than either V-belts or flat belts. There is less wear on the belts or sheaves than on the other two styles of belts. The sheaves are lighter and smaller, which means more compact drives. Speed ratios as high as 40:1 are possible. There's no matching problem, and the belts cannot turn over in the sheaves.

The belts are composed of five basic parts (Fig. 5–18): protective material, belt backing, tension cords, rubber ribs, and synthetic facing. The tension member is comprised of specially treated cords that provide stability and long flex life. The cords are then sealed in a special oil- and heat-resistant material. The

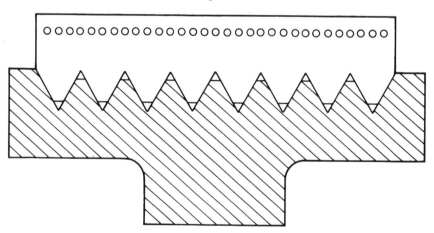

Figure 5-17. Cross section of a ribbed belt.

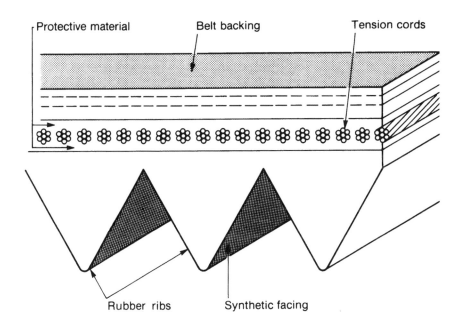

Figure 5-18. Construction of a ribbed belt.

rubber ribs give support to the cords and have a high wear resistance. The ribs are coated with a protective synthetic facing. This allows for maximum wear resistance and protects the ribs from cracking. The backing is oil and abrasion resistant to give the belt cords protection from the environment.

The belts come in five cross sections. H, J, K, L and M, are the most common. The belt code is as follows: 1120 L 16. From that number you would get an "L" section belt. It would have a pitch length of 112.0 inches. The belt would have sixteen ribs on it.

As with the other belts, the alignment of the sheaves is important. They can be aligned in the same manner as described for V-belts. When tensioning ribbed belts, the manufacturer's recommendations should be obtained from the belt distributor and these should be followed. The care and troubleshooting of these will be the same as for the other style belts.

While there are other types of specialty belts, such as double angle, open ended, notched, and steel cable, the previous belts comprise the largest percentage of belts currently in use in plants and facilities. For specifics on specialty belts, contact the manufacturer or distributor of the belt.

Summary

Belt drives are common in industry today. Technicians work on these drive systems frequently. The proper care and maintenance of these systems is important to the life of the drives. Proper installation of these belt drives is also very important. The drives require little maintenance. A technician should be able to identify any drive problems by merely looking at the drive or listening to it. Once a problem is spotted, it should be corrected before damage occurs to the belt.

Belt drives come in a large variety of sizes and shapes. At least one type of belt can be used in almost any drive condition. Once proper selection is made and proper care given, the drive should have a worry-free service life.

Chapter 6:
Roller Chain Fundamentals

V-belts are used to transmit power between components with long center-to-center distances. V-belts are not positive drives. Some slippage may occur under heavy loads. If this slippage is objectionable, a roller chain drive may have to be used.

Roller chain is a flexible and positive method of transmitting power between shafts at long center distances. The chain can be very efficient, if it is kept well lubricated.

Roller Chain Links

A standard roller chain is composed of two basic links: the *pin* and *roller* (Fig. 6–1). The pins are pressed into the link plates and do not rotate. The bushings are pressed into the roller link plate and the roller part of it *does* rotate. The pin and roller joint provides the pivoting action necessary for the chain to travel around the sprocket. The roller is free to rotate around the bushing. The roller must not be held by the roller link plate, There must also be clearances between the roller link plate and the pin link plate to provide the freedom to pivot. When

Figure 6-1.   Pin and roller links. *(Courtesy of P.T. Components, Inc.)*

the chain is lubricated, the lubricant must be thin enough to penetrate between all of the above mentioned areas.

Lubrication is the most important maintenance consideration in dealing with roller chain (see Fig. 6–2). Roller chain wears 300 times faster unlubricated than it does when it's properly lubricated. If a roller chain was designed to last a service life of 7 years and is run unlubricated, it would have an estimated life of 9 days. Certainly this shows the importance of proper lubrication.

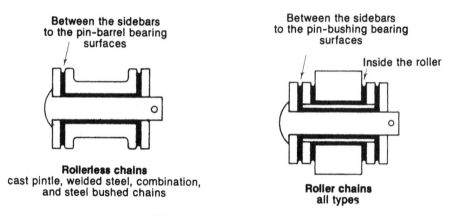

Figure 6-2. Areas of lubricant penetration. *(Courtesy of P.T. Components, Inc.)*

Two other links that may be seen in a roller chain installation are the *connecting* and the *offset* link (Fig. 6–3). The connecting link is used to make a roller chain endless. It looks like a standard pin link except that one of the link plates will not be pressed on the pins. It will have slightly larger holes cut into the plates. This allows the link plate to be slipped over the pins. Some means will be provided to prevent the link plate from coming off the pins, usually cotter pins or a spring clip. Two types of connecting links are presently manufactured. With one type, the link plate slips over the pins easily; the other type requires a slight press force to put the link plate over the pins. Both types will, however, still have some retainer to keep the link plate in position.

One other point to keep in mind, when installing a connecting link, is to push the link plate out against the retainer once the installation is complete. This

Figure 6-3. Connecting and offset links. *(Courtesy of P.T. Components, Inc.)*

allows the lubricant to penetrate the area between the link plate and to get into the roller–bushing–pin joints.

The offset link is the other link used in roller chain. The offset link is also used to connect roller chain. It will, however, leave the chain with an odd number of pitches. This link can be used to adjust the length of a chain when the center-to-center distance of the sprockets can't be adjusted. It shouldn't be used unless there's no other option because it isn't as strong as a standard roller chain link.

All four of the standard roller chain links are case hardened. This means that they have a hardened outer surface, but the inner surface is a softer material. When the chain is worn enough that the hardened surface is worn away, it should be replaced. This will usually be about a 3% wear. If you have a length of roller chain 100 inches long, and after removing it from service it is 103 or more inches long, it's worn to the state that it must be replaced. Failure to do so will result in a broken chain during operation, and subsequent loss of operation from the equipment.

The standard roller chain sizing code is important for the maintenance technician to understand (see Table 6–1). The sizing is standard in industry and is simpler than the belt coding system. The length code is divided into the eighths

Table 6-1 Chain Sizing Code

Chain Number	Pitch (in inches)	Type of Roller Chain
25	$1/4$	Rollerless links
30	$3/8$	Standard links
35	$3/8$	Rollerless links
40	$1/2$	Standard links
41	$1/2$	Light duty, narrow links
50	$5/8$	Standard links
60	$3/4$	Standard links
60-H	$3/4$	Heavy series links
80	1	Standard links
100	$1\,1/4$	Standard links
120	$1\,1/2$	Standard links
140	$1\,3/4$	Standard links
160	2	Standard links
180	$2\,1/4$	Standard links
200	$2\,1/2$	Standard links
240	3	Standard links

Note: Any chain sized above the 60 series may have the -H designation.

Note: Any chain having a -2, -3, -4H, etc., is designated as having that number of strands.

system. The first digit (or in the case of larger chain, the first two digits) indicates the pitch length in eighths of an inch. If you have a 40 chain, the pitch length is $^4/_8$ or $^1/_2$ inch. The zero indicates that it's standard roller chain. A 60 chain would have a pitch of $^6/_8$ or $^3/_4$ inch and is standard roller chain.

A 25 chain would have a pitch of $^2/_8$ or $^1/_4$ inch, but the 5 indicates that it's rollerless chain. The roller is left off because of the small size, and the bushing has direct contact with the sprocket. This style of chain is usually found in the small sizes only (25, 35 being the most popular). A 41 chain has a pitch of $^4/_8$ or $^1/_2$ inch, and the 1 indicates that the chain is light chain, meaning it's narrow and for lighter loads. A 60-H chain is a $^6/_8$ or $^3/_4$ inch pitch chain with a heavy series designation. This means that the side plates are thicker than in normal chain. In fact, the 60-H chain has the same thickness link plate as the 80 standard series chain. The heavy series chain does not start until the size 60. From 60 up to the larger sizes, the heavy designation may be found.

One last variable in the code is the strand number. This number is only used if the chain is more than 1 strand wide. For example, an 80-3 is an $^8/_8$ or 1-inch pitch chain that is 3 strands wide. The purpose of having more than 1 strand is to increase the horsepower rating of the chain.

Installation of Roller Chain

For proper installation of a roller chain, use the following steps.

1. Remove the old chain and clean the sprockets.
2. Check the alignment of the sprockets.
3. Check the sprocket for excessive wear. If the teeth become hook shaped, they will damage a new chain.
4. Lay the new chain over the sprockets and connect.
5. Increase the sprocket's center-to-center distance to tension correctly (approximately 2% sag at the center of the strand).
6. Check for proper lubrication.
7. Start drive and recheck tension after 24 hours of run time. Retension if necessary.

Roller Chain Wear

When a roller chain wears, the pin and bushing joint clearances increase, making it appear that the chain has stretched. Since only the outer surfaces are hardened (Fig. 6–4), once they are worn away the softer inner core must bear the load. Since it's soft, it wears quickly, and chain failure results in a short time period. As the wear progresses and the chain does lengthen, it begins to ride higher on the sprocket teeth. This increases the loading forces on the chain and sprocket. As a general rule, a 3% elongation is all that can be tolerated before

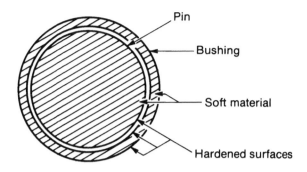

Figure 6-4. Enlarged pin and bushing joint.

the chain should be replaced. At this point most of the hardened surfaces on the chain bushing and joints can be considered to be worn away. While this is a good general rule, sprockets having large numbers of teeth can tolerate slightly more elongation. The best way to measure the elongation is to remove the chain and lay it on a flat clean surface. If you have a 100-inch section of chain and it measures 103 inches, replacement should be made.

Types of Chain Failure

When a chain failure does occur, it's important to inspect the chain to dertimine the cause. Roller chain failures usually can be classified in three categories: wear, fatigue, and ultimate strength.

Wear can be broken into two categories: chain or sprocket. As previously stated, as a chain wears it appears to elongate. This elongation between the links causes it to ride high on the sprocket teeth. When the links go through the slack side of the chain, there will eventually be enough slack chain for it to jump a tooth. This will cause shock loading and accelerate chain wear, possibly even breaking the chain. The most common cause for this wear is the lack of the proper lubricant. When metal-to-metal contact (poor lubrication) in the pin and bushing joint occurs, metal is quickly removed. With this hardened outer material removed, the softer material wears even faster. Premature failure quickly follows.

One other way the wear may occur is when abrasive material gets on the chain and works itself into the chain joint. This is similar to taking sandpaper to the chain, and rapidly removing chain metal, resulting in the elongation of the pin and bushing area.

Sprocket wear is a normal occurrence in any drive. The contact between the chain and sprocket teeth causes eventual metal removal even under the best lubricating conditions. The sprocket doesn't have to be changed every time the chain is replaced, for a sprocket may outlast two or three replacement chains. However, when chain replacement has become excessive, thought should be given to possible sprocket replacement. The worn sprocket will greatly accelerate chain wear due to the loading that occurs when the chain isn't riding in the designated area on the sprocket tooth.

Fatigue failure can occur in any component of the chain. The link plate will almost always experience a fatigue failure near the hole in the plate (either the pin or the bushing). The crack that develops is due to an overload that exceeds the rating of the link plate but does not exceed its ultimate strength. This repeated stressing causes the crack to expand and finally breaks the link plate. The loading of the chain should be checked to ensure that the manufacturer's recommendations aren't exceeded.

Bushing fatigue failures occur in a drive system due to continuous overloads. The cracks from the overstressing of the bushing form in two ways. The first way is a crack running the length of the bushing, usually caused by too hard an impact of the chain with the sprocket teeth. The second way a failure occurs is by a circumference crack around the bushing at the link plate. Either type can be prevented by reducing the load on the chain to a level that doesn't exceed the manufacturer's recommendation.

Roller fatigue failures are caused by the impact of the chain on the sprocket teeth. This may also cause bushing failure due to the transfer of load from the roller to the bushing. However, the roller isn't affected by the load as much as the bushing. The main way the roller is affected is by the speed of the drive. The faster the chain runs, the more shock the roller must absorb as the two come together. The roller may also absorb high loads if the chain is jumping teeth on the sprocket. The constant overloading causes the roller to fatigue. The cure, then, becomes obvious: reduce the speed for the size chain, or correct the problem causing the chain to jump teeth.

Pin fatigue failure rarely occurs in a chain drive, for the pin has a fatigue strength far greater than the other chain parts. Sometimes an overload will occur, thus beginning a crack in the pin, and progressing to a failure that appears to be a fatigue failure. When this occurs it's virtually impossible to detect the difference. Using a higher rated chain or reducing the load is the only cure for this condition.

Ultimate strength failures occur in link plates, bushings, and pins from a large overload being applied as a sudden shock to the drive. This may occur as a sudden shock, or with a normal load and the chain jumping sprocket teeth. In either case, the failure is difficult to distinguish from a fatigue failure. Rollers will very rarely fail in ultimate strength. Due to their position, the overload would be transferred to another component in the chain joint causing it to fail.

Common Chain Problems

The following is a discussion of the most common chain problems and a possible correction for each.

Chain misalignment can cause a variety of problems. It can cause the drive to be noisy and have stiff chain joints, and can cause wear on the sides of the sprocket teeth and inside of the roller link plates (Fig. 6–5).

Figure 6-5.   Wear on inside of roller link plates.

One of the best methods to check the alignment is to use a piece of string as illustrated in Fig. 6–6. If the string doesn't touch on all four points indicated, adjustment should be made so that it does in order to ensure proper alignment.

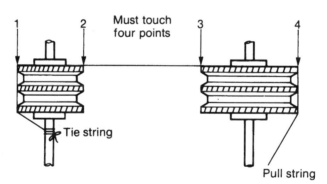

Figure 6-6.   String alignment method.

Worn-out chains cause the drive to be noisy, but they'll also ride high on the sprocket teeth, even causing the chain to jump teeth in the drive. This may also cause broken chain components. The only solution is to replace the chain. Remember, in most cases, replacing a worn link or section of chain with a new link or section of chain will accelerate wear on the drive. The forces that are introduced in the drive with new and worn components operating together in the chain will dramatically increase the wear rate. The best practice is to replace the entire chain.

Improper tension can cause the drive to be noisy and the chain to climb the sprocket teeth; it can also cause chain whip. Adjusting the tension to a 2% deflection of the center distance on the slack side will remedy the situation (see Fig. 6–7).

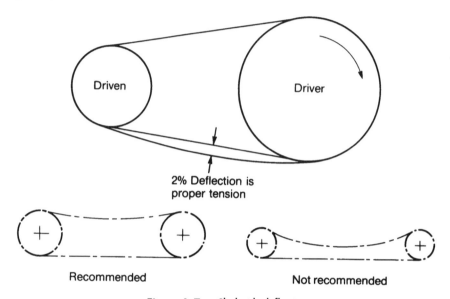

Figure 6-7. Slack side deflection.

Improper lubrication causes the chain to run hot, develop stiff joints, or run noisily. If too thick lubricant is used, it may cause the chain joint to try to stay on the sprocket. This can be remedied by using the lubricant recommended by the manufacturer for your application. If the information cannot be found, a good rule of thumb is to use a 30 weight oil in a standard application, with an ambient temperature of 60 – 90°F. When operating outside this range, adjust the grade of oil accordingly.

Roller Chain Sprockets

Roller chain sprockets come in three basic designs: detachable hub, single hub, and double hub.

Detachable hubs use some form of an incline plane principle to wedge the sprocket to the shaft. Some form of Allen screws or hex headed bolts are used to tighten the sprocket to the hub. Most manufacturers supply auxiliary tapped holes for the purpose of forcing the sprocket back off the hub. The various manufacturers usually provide a comprehensive selection of bushing sizes for the sprocket. This has the advantage of allowing the sprocket to be used on various sized shafting. This design is very practical where frequent installation and removal must be made.

The **single hub** and **double hub** are used on a shaft with a key and set screw. They are usually bored to size, which limits their use to one shaft size only. The size of the transmitted load determines the choice of the single or double sprocket.

While roller chain is commonly used in industry, it must be maintained to make the investment in this form of power transmission. The technician must give consideration to the type of drive, maintenance requirements, and the repair frequency. When these points are kept in mind, the chain drive will deliver the long and trusted service life that it was designed to deliver.

Silent Chain

Silent chain is another form of chain that is popular in power transmission . It has the following *advantages* over roller chain:

• higher operating speeds,
• more efficient,
• longer life, and
• quieter and smoother operation.

The *disadvantage* of the silent chain is that it's more expensive than roller chain. Unlike standard roller chain, silent chain has two dimensions that must be specified when ordering. In addition to the pitch, the thickness must be specified. For example, SC-8-08 means:

• SC-silent chain
• 8-pitch in eighths $^8/_8$ or 1 inch
• 08-thickness in fourths – $^8/_4$ or 2 inches thick.

In any silent chain installation, careful inspection should be given to the silent chain sprocket. If the silent chain sprocket is center guide or double center guide, then that's the only chain that can be used with it. When the thicknesses are the same, then side guide chains can be interchanged.

Maintenance of silent chain is very similar to that of roller chain. Lubrication and alignment are of primary importance. In alignment, care should be taken to inspect the chain and sprocket guide. Any tendency to wear on one side of the guide and sprocket will indicate an alignment problem, and prompt attention should be given to the drive. Lack of the proper lubricant will shorten the life of the drive to a fraction of what it's designed to deliver—similar to the wear rate on roller chain.

Summary

Roller chain is a positive means of transmitting power between shafts with long center distances. The advantage it has over V-belts is positive drive. The advantage it has over gears is the flexibility. If the maintenance guidelines outlined here are followed, the chain drive will have a long service life with a minimum of maintenance problems.

Chapter 7:
Gear Drive Fundamentals

Introduction

In a belt drive, the pulleys are driven by the frictional contact from the belt. Now picture the pulleys pressed together. The pulleys are not the ideal frictional surface and would have a problem with slippage. The slippage would be eliminated if the outer circumference could be cut or notched so that the pulleys would engage as they rotate. This is the basic idea behind a gear. While the tooth design may vary from gear to gear, the principle is the same: gears may be defined as two or more circular discs that transmit power or torque by the engaging of consecutive teeth.

Gear drives are among the earliest forms of power transmission devices. They're used to transmit power, change speed, or change rotation of shafts. They can be used to transmit power between shafts at right angles, between parallel shafts, or between shafts whose center lines don't intersect or aren't in the same plane.

When gears have different numbers of teeth in mesh, the one with the smaller number of teeth is called the *pinion* and the one with the larger number of teeth is called the gear. Gear drives are usually divided into two main classifications: those with a parallel shaft axis and those with shafts that intersect at various angles.

First, we will cover the gear drives that have a parallel shaft axis. They are called spur, helical, herringbone, internal, and rack and pinion gears. Fig. 7–1 (a–g) illustrates some of the basic terms associated with these gears.

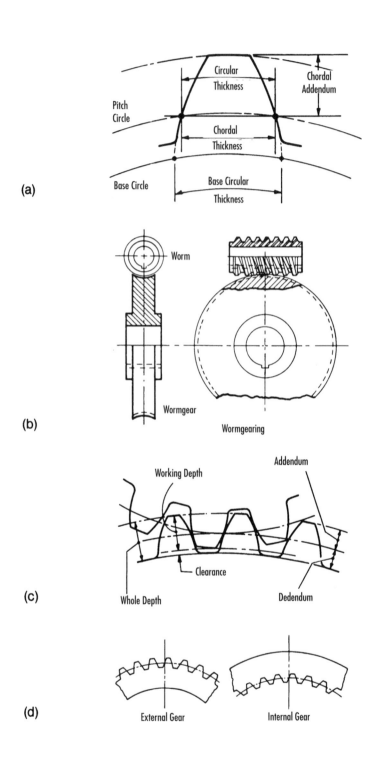

(a)

(b)

(c)

(d)

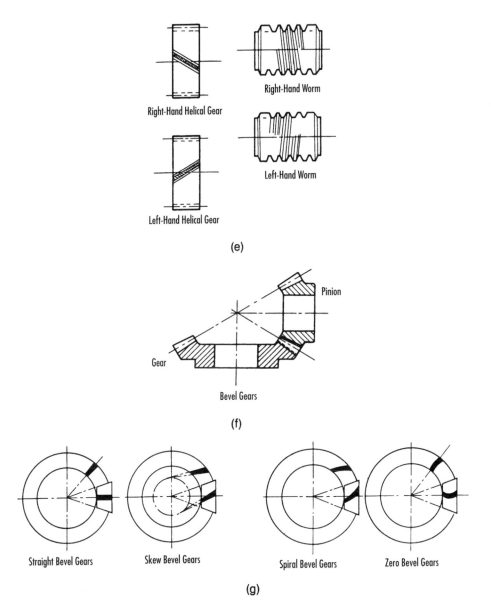

Right-Hand Helical Gear

Right-Hand Worm

Left-Hand Helical Gear

Left-Hand Worm

(e)

Pinion

Gear

Bevel Gears

(f)

Straight Bevel Gears   Skew Bevel Gears   Spiral Bevel Gears   Zero Bevel Gears

(g)

Figure 7-1 (a-g).   Basic gear terms.

Spur Gears

The spur gear (Fig. 7–2) has the teeth cut parallel to the shaft axis. It is the basic type, and all other parallel shaft gears are derived from the spur. When the teeth are in contact or mesh, the power is transmitted by a combined sliding and

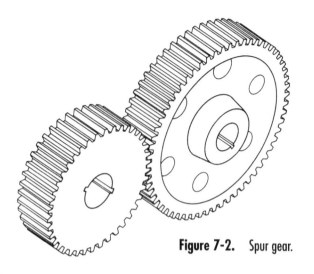

Figure 7-2.   Spur gear.

rolling action between the teeth. The ease of manufacture, low cost, and ease of maintenance make the spur gear one of the most popular designs.

Helical Gears

The helical gear (Fig. 7–3) was derived from the spur to allow for higher speeds and higher loads.

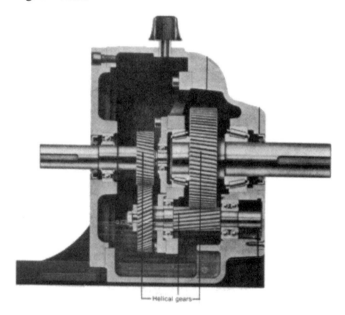

Figure 7-3.   Helical gears. *(Courtesy of P.T. Components, Inc.)*

Instead of the teeth being cut parallel to the shaft axis, they're cut at an angle. The angle they're cut at is called the *helix angle*. This creates more of a problem when matching gears, since there are many different helix angles: 7–23 degrees being the most common. For the gears to properly mesh, they must not only have the same helix angle, but must also be of different "hands." This means that one must have the teeth cut in the right-hand direction and the other in the left-hand direction.

Since the teeth are cut at an angle, there will always be more tooth surface in contact when in mesh. This allows for greater strength, and also allows for a quieter and smoother drive. The tooth angle also creates yet another problem. The angle at which the teeth are cut produces an end thrust when the gears are rotated. The greater the helix angle, the greater the end thrust produced. Any application designed for helical gears must also have bearings and other drive components capable of withstanding the end thrust produced.

One type of helical gear that doesn't fall into the parallel shaft gear category is the crossed axis or the *spiral gear* (Fig. 7–4). These helical gears have a 45-degree helix angle and can be run on right angle drives. The difference in these drives is that the hand or the cut of the teeth must be the same to run at right angles. Since the teeth run at right angles, there isn't much surface contact of the teeth. This limits the use of this type of gear to only light loads.

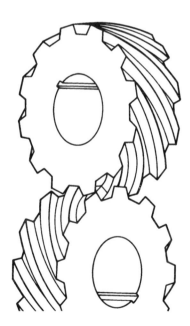

Figure 7-4.   Spiral gears. *(Courtesy of American Gear Manufacturers Association)*

Herringbone Gears

The herringbone gear (Fig. 7–5) is basically a helical gear with both a right-hand and a left-hand set of teeth on the same gear. In fact, the herringbone gear is also called a double helical gear. These gear teeth have the advantage of having more tooth surface in contact, and so are stronger and quieter, and produce no end thrust. Because it has both left- and right-handed teeth, the two end thrusts that are generated cancel each other. The herringbone gear is the strongest and smoothest gear, and is capable of higher speeds than any other parallel shaft gear. It's also the most expensive gear to manufacture. For that reason, you'll find it in application only where the spur or helical gears cannot be used.

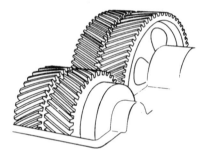

Figure 7-5.   Herringbone gear. *(Courtesy of American Gear Manufacturers Association)*

Internal Gear

The internal gear (Fig. 7–6) has the gear teeth cut inside the gear, and a mating pinion that meshes inside the gear. The large outer gear is sometimes referred to as the *annular* gear. The gear drive may also have more than one internal gear. These types of drives are called *planetary* drives (Fig. 7–7). The small drive is called the *sun* gear; the others are called the planets and the ring (or annulus) gear. The teeth are usually of the spur cut, but may also be helical or herringbone.

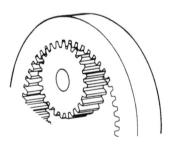

Figure 7-6.   Internal gear. *(Courtesy of American Gear Manufacturers Association)*

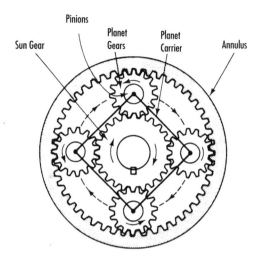

Figure 7-7.   Planetary gears.

Rack and Pinion Gears

The rack and pinion (Fig. 7–8) is used to convert rotary motion into linear motion, or linear motion into rotary motion. This is accomplished by a flat rack with teeth cut into the face of the rack meshed with a pinion. The rack and pinion has either spur, helical, or herringbone teeth. The design requirements versus the cost determine what type will be used.

Gears with right angle applications are divided into two basic categories, worm and bevel.

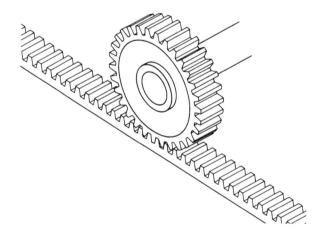

Figure 7-8.   Rack and pinion.

Worm Gears

The worm gear (Fig. 7–9) is capable of transmitting large amounts of power. As the gear ratio (which increases or decreases the speed) becomes greater, the efficiency decreases, which limits the use of the worm gear. In a worm drive there are two parts, the worm and the worm gear. The worm is usually made of steel or some stronger alloy, while the worm gear is usually made from brass or bronze or a softer alloy. The worm is usually the driver; however, drives having a ratio of less than 30:1 can be back driven. In applying gear ratios to worm drives, the ratio 30:1 means that for every 30 revolutions of the worm, the gear would turn once. Any worm gear drive with a ratio of 30:1 or greater is called a self-locking drive, meaning it cannot be back driven. To change the ratio in a drive, a worm gear with a different number of teeth can be installed. The worm can also affect the drive by having more than one start or lead on it. If it has more than one start (usually six is maximum), it turns the worm gear faster. For example, a 3-start or lead turns the gear 3 times as fast as a single.

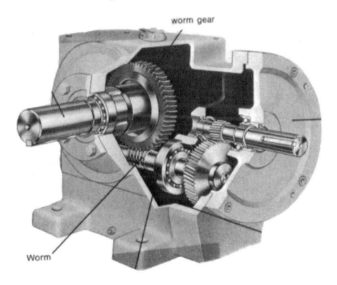

Figure 7-9.   Worm and worm gear. *(Courtesy of P.T. Components, Inc.)*

Bevel Gears

Bevel gears are very versatile as angle drives. There are four types: straight, spiral, zerol, and hypoid.

Bevel gears (Fig. 7–10) have their teeth cut on cones. Depending on the type of gear, the teeth may be straight, spiraled, or a combination. The axis may intersect at a given angle or not at all. They're efficient and work where worm drives cannot.

Straight bevel gears have teeth that, if they were extended, would converge at the center of the gear. They usually run at shaft intersection angles of 90 degrees, but may be found at angles less than 90 degrees (acute) or more than 90 degrees (obtuse). If two straight bevel gears are in mesh and have the same number of teeth, and are at a 90 degree shaft intersection angle, they're called miter gears.

Spiral bevel gears have the same shape as straight bevel gears except the teeth have a helix angle. This type affords the same advantages as the helical gears. The spiral teeth allow for more tooth surface to be in contact at any time, and make a smoother and quieter drive.

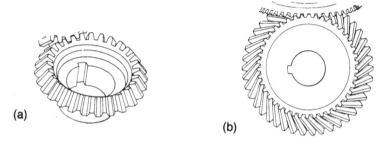

(a)

(b)

Figure 7-10.   Bevel gears: (a) straight and (b) spiral.
(Courtesy of American Gear Manufacturers Association)

Zerol bevel gears are a combination of the straight and the spiral bevel gears. They have teeth that are cut so they would intersect in the center of the gear, but they're cut on a machine that cuts the spiral teeth, so they're a straight spiral tooth. The advantage is that there is no thrust set up by the helix angle, but the shape of the tooth still provides more tooth surface in contact than in the straight bevel gear.

Hypoid gears (Fig. 7–11) are spiral bevel gears that have axes that don't intersect. This is a great advantage on heavier drives, for the shafts can be extended and support can be given to each end of the shaft.

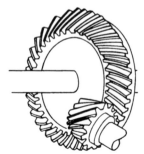

Figure 7-11.   Hypoid gears.
(Courtesy of American Gear Manufacturers Association)

Lubrication of Gears

In all gear drives, lubrication is a prime consideration. The function of the lubricant is to build a wedge to prevent metal-to-metal contact. Selection of the correct lubricant is extremely important to obtain maximum life from a gear drive. If the lubricant is too thin, it is not able to separate the mating surfaces under load. The film barrier will rupture and metal-to-metal contact occurs. The surfaces in direct contact under load will generate intense heat. The surface asperities will weld together and then tear apart when coming out of mesh. This welding and tearing results in rapid deterioration of the gear tooth profile. If the lubricant is too thick, it won't enter the meshing gears, and won't build the wedge with the same results.

Equally important is the proper filtration of the lubricating fluid. If foreign material is allowed between the teeth while in mesh, the material will be imbedded into the tooth surface, or it will scratch the tooth surface as it slides into and out of mesh. If possible, a filter with a 3-micron rating is suggested for all recirculating lubrication systems.

Lubrication Methods

Lubrication systems for gears are divided into four categories: splash, slinger, drip, and spray.

Splash method. The splash method has a fluid level in an enclosed case high enough to be picked up by the lower gear. As a gear rotates, it splashes oil into the case in sufficient quantity to lubricate the gear system.

Slinger method. The slinger method has an eccentric disc located on the shaft. This disc dips into the oil, picking up a sufficient quantity to lubricate the gears.

Drip and spray methods. The drip and spray methods are both used on higher speed drives. The system must have an external pump to provide flow of lubricant. The drip uses a small orifice to allow very slow feed of the lubricant to the desired location in the gearcase. The spray uses a higher flow rate allowing the maximum lubrication to the desired areas in the gearcase.

Backlash

Working hand in hand with the lubricant is the backlash in a gear drive. Backlash is the amount of clearance that the manufacturer designs into a gear. This clearance is designed into the gear itself (Fig. 7–12). A small amount of material is removed from the tooth surface to provide this clearance. This enables the teeth to enter and leave the mesh without binding, and it also leaves enough clearance for the lubricant to enter the mesh to help protect the gear tooth.

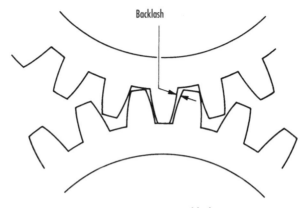

Figure 7-12. Backlash.

Gear Tooth Failure

It's important to be able to recognize wear patterns on the teeth. This enables the maintenance technician to recognize potential problems before they become so severe that the drive is damaged or destroyed. It may also prevent the installation of replacement gears when a problem still exists. The American Gear Manufacturer's Association divides gear tooth wear and failures into four categories: wear, surface fatigue, plastic flow, and breakage.

Wear is merely a normal function of the gear design whereby the metal is removed from the gear tooth in the contact areas of the tooth. There are seven basic types of wear (Fig. 7–13):

1. *Normal.* Normal wear results in a smoothing or polishing of the tooth surface. This wear ceases once the initial surface asperities are worn away. See Fig. 7-13 (a).

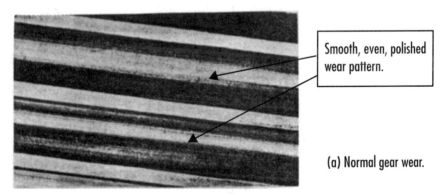

Smooth, even, polished wear pattern.

(a) Normal gear wear.

Figure 7-13. Types of gear wear. *(Courtesy of American Gear Manufacturers Association)*

2. *Moderate*. This wear takes a longer time to develop. It results in removal of material from the addedum and dedendem, but leaves the pitch line virtually untouched. A higher viscosity lubricant usually stops this type of wear. If that doesn't work, increasing the speed will help to build the wedge of lubricant. See Fig. 7–13 (b).

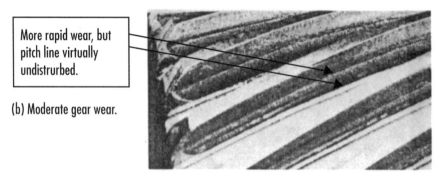

More rapid wear, but pitch line virtually undistrurbed.

(b) Moderate gear wear.

3. *Destructive*. This is a heavier wear that removes enough material to change the shape of the gear tooth. It's usually noticed by excessive noise during operation. This wear can be corrected by the same methods as for moderate wear. See Fig. 7–13 (c).

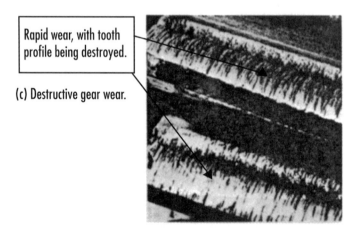

Rapid wear, with tooth profile being destroyed.

(c) Destructive gear wear.

4. *Abrasive*. This is identified by scratches in the tooth in the direction of the mesh. It is caused by particles in the lube. Increase filtration to prevent abrasion. See Fig. 7–13 (d).

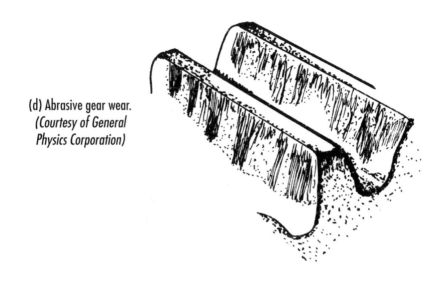

(d) Abrasive gear wear.
*(Courtesy of General
Physics Corporation)*

5. *Scratching*. This is severe abrasion caused by larger particles passing through the mesh, and it can be eliminated by better filtration or more frequent oil changes. See Fig. 7–13 (e).

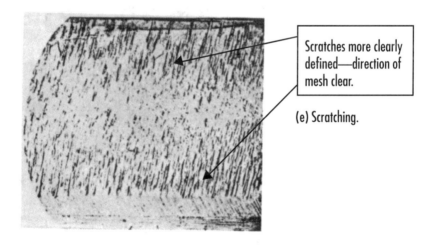

Scratches more clearly defined—direction of mesh clear.

(e) Scratching.

6. *Scoring*. This is metal removal by welding and tearing. It can look like frosting or can have obvious weld and tear markings in the direction of the sliding mesh. It can be across the whole tooth or may be in a localized area of the tooth. Scoring is caused by failure of the fluid barrier to prevent metal-to-metal contact. A high viscosity lubricant or one with an extreme pressure additive is recommended. See Fig. 7–13 (f).

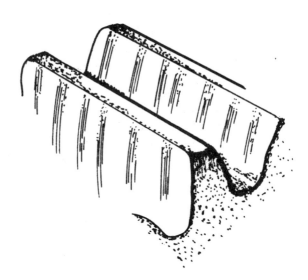

(f) Scoring.
(Courtesy of General
Physics Corporation)

7. *Interference*. This condition occurs where there is excessive backlash in a set of gears. There's heavy wear at the root of the tooth. It can only be corrected by a design change. See Fig. 7–13 (g).

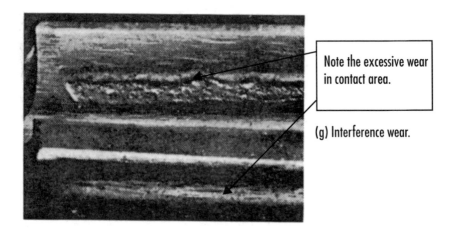

Note the excessive wear in contact area.

(g) Interference wear.

Surface fatigue occurs when the tooth surface is stressed beyond its design limits. This results in the contacting asperities being fatigued and removed, and thus leaves pits. This may continue until the tooth is destroyed. There are three types of surface fatigue (Fig. 7–14).

1. *Initial pitting.* This type leaves very small pits, and is usually caused by some design flaw in the tooth. It generally occurs when the tooth profiles don't match correctly. It's usually self-correcting. See Fig. 7-14 (a).

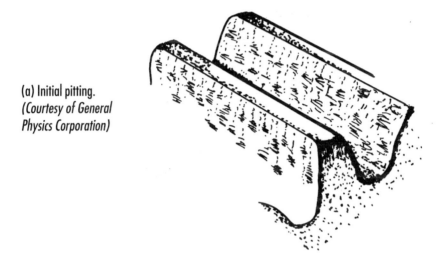

(a) Initial pitting. *(Courtesy of General Physics Corporation)*

2. *Destructive pitting.* This generally results from a tooth running under loads higher than it is rated to carry. Reducing the load is the only cure. See Fig. 7–14 (b).

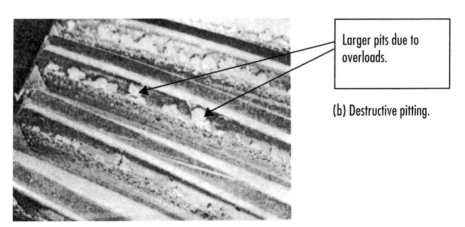

Larger pits due to overloads.

(b) Destructive pitting.

3. *Spalling.* This is similar to pitting, except that the craters are very shallow. The spalling may advance so that the craters join, thus leaving larger ones, and it may continue until the tooth is destroyed. Reducing the load is the cure for spalling. See Fig. 7–14 (c).

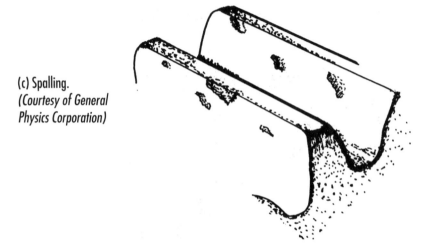

(c) Spalling.
(Courtesy of General
Physics Corporation)

Plastic flow is the movement of subsurface material on a gear tooth face. It is caused by high contact *stresses* or overloads. There are three basic types of plastic flow (Fig. 7–15).

1. *Rolling and peening.* This is the movement of material to the ends of the gear teeth. It's usually apparent by the fins at the tips of the teeth. The rolling occurs with the sliding continuous overload. The peening occurs with heavier, hammering loads. This usually indicates the drive is running with a too high load. See Fig. 7–15 (a).

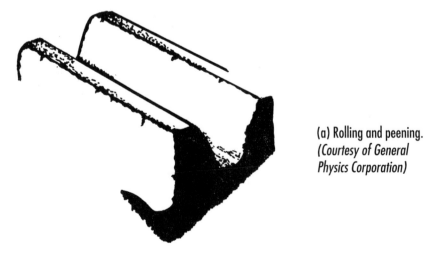

(a) Rolling and peening.
(Courtesy of General
Physics Corporation)

2. *Rippling.* The gear will have a fish scale appearance, caused by the movement of the subsurface material. This problem is again related to heavy loads, but may be remedied by a lubricant with an extreme pressure additive. See Fig. 7–15 (b).

(b) Rippling.
*(Courtesy of General
Physics Corporation)*

3. *Ridging.* This is also caused by heavy loads. The condition appears as ridges in the gear tooth. The ridges run in the direction of the sliding of the mesh. It may even have the appearance of scratching. The best remedy is to reduce the load, or use a lubricant with an extreme pressure additive. See Fig. 7–15 (c).

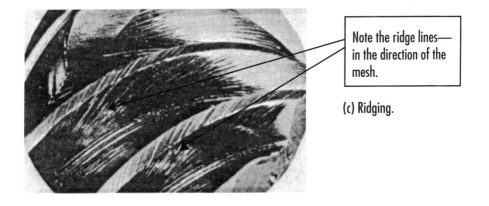

Note the ridge lines—
in the direction of the
mesh.

(c) Ridging.

Breakage is the removal of a tooth or part of a tooth. It is caused by an overload of the gear drive — either one shock load, or continuous overloading of the teeth. There are two basic types of breakage (Fig. 7–16).

1. *Fatigue*. This is caused by repeated overloads, resulting in small stress cracks, which eventually cause the tooth to break off the gear. Reducing the loads or redesigning the drive are the only cures. See Fig. 7–16 (a).

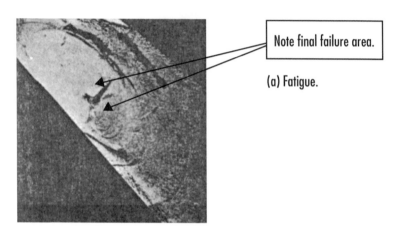

Note final failure area.

(a) Fatigue.

2. *Overload*. Overload results when one sudden shock load is severe enough to remove the tooth from the gear. This may be caused by foreign material wedging in the mesh causing an overload. Continuous monitoring of the loads and correcting the overloads are the only cures. See Fig. 7–16 (b).

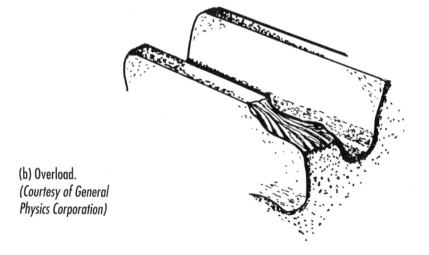

(b) Overload.
(Courtesy of General
Physics Corporation)

By observing their condition and carefully maintaining the gears, life expectancy can be greatly extended. If failures do occur, the cause should be identified and corrected before a replacement is installed.

Summary

Properly maintained gear drives will deliver almost infinite service lives. They're capable of changing speeds, changing direction, and changing torque in any drive. Maintaining a gear drive must involve careful inspections to observe wear patterns on the different gears. Knowing the wear patterns will enable a technician to spot trouble before failure of the drive results.

Chapter 8:
Coupling Fundamentals

Types of Couplings

Couplings are used to connect mechanical drives to a prime mover, and they are found in all industries. They fall into two broad classifications: mechanical and fluid. In this text, mechanical couplings will be discussed.

Mechanical couplings can be further divided into three classifications, rigid, flexible, and universal joint (Fig. 8-1).

Rigid couplings are used where two shafts must be directly coupled. The alignment is critical, because there's no play in a rigid coupling. The two main types of rigid couplings are the flanged and the sleeve. Flange couplings are

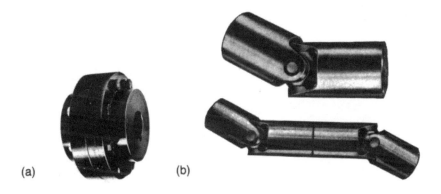

(a)   (b)

Figure 8-1. (a) Flange coupling, (b) single and double universal joints. *(Courtesy of P.T. Components, Inc.)*

111

used in heavy duty applications, with large shafts and heavy loads. Sleeve couplings are used in smaller applications where shaft sizes are less than six inches.

Flexible couplings are made to compensate for some slight shaft misalignment. There are four types of misalignment that may be encountered in aligning a coupling: angular, parallel, combination angular parallel, and shaft float.

Flexible couplings can compensate for one or, in some cases, all four types of misalignment. But flexible couplings are not cure-alls. Just because they are labeled flexible doesn't mean they can compensate for ridiculous amounts of misalignment. If a manufacturer says its coupling can compensate for 0.005 misalignment, it still should be aligned as close as possible before startup. An illustration of this might be made using a car speedometer. Just because the speedometer goes to 120 mph, you don't drive it that fast everywhere you travel. The same can be said for a coupling; just because it says 0.005", it doesn't mean it should run with that much misalignment. As a general rule, the higher the speed of the coupling, the less misalignment that can be tolerated.

The more common flexible couplings shown in Fig. 8-2 all use play in the coupling to compensate for misalignment.

(a) Gear.

(c) Chain.

(b) Grid.

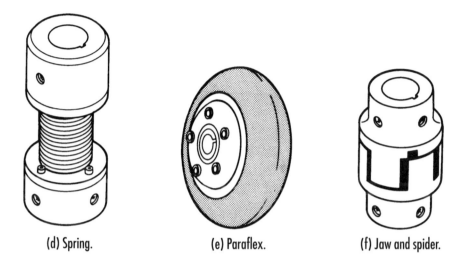

| (d) Spring. | (e) Paraflex. | (f) Jaw and spider. |

Figure 8-2 (a-f).   Common flexible couplings.

Universal Joints

The universal joint is used where severe misalignment is encountered. There are two basic types of universal joints, the single and the double. The single universal joint can compensate for angular misalignment, and the double universal joint can compensate for offset and parallel misalignment. If there is to be a change in the angle of misalignment, then a special slipped shaft, splined universal joint must be used.

Installing couplings

When installing any coupling there are a variety of problems that may be encountered. The following is intended to be a guide to installation. The first step is to determine if all components are in place and ready to assemble. This would include determining if the hub of the coupling is a *clearance fit* or an *interference fit*. A clearance fit has some means of locking the coupling on the shaft once it's slid into place. An interference fit means that the coupling hub has to be heated before it's installed to provide the proper clearance to get it on the shaft.

Heating the Coupling

There are two main methods for heating a coupling before it's installed: the oil bath and the air oven.

1. *Oil bath*. The oil bath is a fast way to heat the hub, but you're limited to a maximum temperature of 350°F. When using an oil bath, care should be taken that the hub doesn't rest on the bottom of the tank in direct contact with the heating source.
2. *Air oven*. The air oven is able to heat the hub to a higher temperature, but it's not as fast. Care should be taken so as not to allow the coupling to be heated above 600°F, because above this temperature the coupling steel will react with the air. One advantage of the air oven over the oil bath is that the coupling can be handled with heat resistant gloves, for it will not be slippery as it would in the oil bath.

Key size

Another problem area when installing couplings is the key. If the key is not the correct size, it will result in premature coupling failure. If the key is loose in the keyway, it will, over a period of time, work back and forth in the keyway enough to begin wearing the keyway and the key. When this type of wear has progressed enough, the coupling half may actually be able to turn on the shaft. When this occurs, the coupling is useless and will have to be replaced. The other problem is having a too tall key in the coupling (see Fig. 8–3). This prevents the hub from having a proper fit on the shaft, and could set up stresses that split the coupling hub. The key should have a tight sliding fit in the keyway when it's correctly installed.

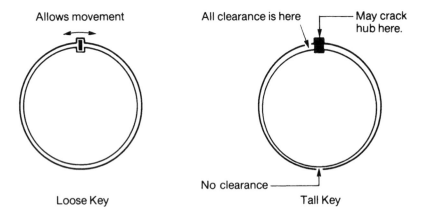

Figure 8-3.   Loose and tall key.

Coupling Bolts

Coupling bolts can be another problem area during installation. Coupling bolts should be torqued to the recommended values during installation. Too often, the mechanic tightens the bolts by feel, not applying enough torque to properly hold the bolt. Coupling manufacturers also provide special bolts with the couplings. These bolts are usually a grade 8 hardness. They should be replaced with a bolt of the same rating or a higher rating. If the bolts are replaced with a softer bolt, they will stretch and fail prematurely. During installation of the coupling bolts, you should turn the nuts and not the bolts. This will enable the correct amount of tension to be applied to the bolt. However, when removing a bolt from a coupling, it's best to loosen the bolt and not the nut. If a lockwasher is on the assembly and the nut is turned, it'll dig into the coupling and damage the surface the lockwasher is in contact with.

Lubrication

When installing the coupling, it's important to notice where the fittings for lubrication are located. If possible when assembling the coupling, position the fittings 180 degrees apart (Fig. 8–4). This will make relubrication of the coupling easier. By removing both fittings for the lubrication, and positioning them horizontally, the lubricant can be added until it runs out the other side, indicating it is half full, which is the proper level for most flexible gear couplings.

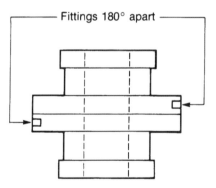

Figure 8-4.   Position of grease fittings.

Alignment of Couplings

It should be noted that there are some very sophisticated tools available for aligning couplings, such as laser alignment. However, the dial indicator method will be presented, since it is still one of the basic methods utilized in most plants and facilities.

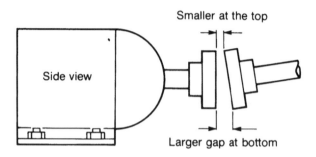

Figure 8-5.   Vertical angular.

Alignment of couplings can be accomplished in a five-step procedure.

1. *Vertical angular.* The vertical angular (Fig. 8–5) alignment can be checked by placing a dial indicator on the driving shaft. Place the tip of the indicator against the other coupling half. Lock the shafts together and rotate the shafts 180 degrees. Notice the difference in the reading on the indicator. This is the amount of misalignment in the vertical angular direction. To determine the size of shims required, use this formula:

$$(D_1 \div D_2) \times R = mT$$

   where D_1 = Distance between the drivers' base bolts
   D_2 = Diameter of the coupling half
   R = Dial indicator reading
   T = Thickness of the shims required.

   Once this is known, place the shims under the base and tighten the base down, and check the reading again to ensure that it was correct. Now you're ready to go to the vertical parallel procedure (Fig. 8–6).

2. *Vertical parallel.* This time, position the dial indicator so that it reads the difference in height of the two coupling halves. This can be read by positioning the indicator on the rim of the coupling. Set at zero, and rotate it 180 degrees. Take half the difference and place that size shim under the base of the driver. Recheck the reading to be sure the shims were the correct size.

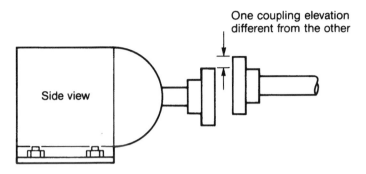

Figure 8-6.   Vertical parallel.

3. *Horizontal angular.* The horizontal angular (Fig. 8–7) is read by placing the dial indicator to read the inside of the coupling halves. This time no shims are required. The shifting of the driver sideways is all that's required to adjust the readings.

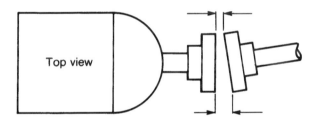

Figure 8-7.   Horizontal angular.

4. *Horizontal parallel.* The horizontal parallel (Fig. 8–8) is read on the outside of the coupling half. It's adjusted by shifting the driver until it's in alignment.

5. The final step is to go back and recheck the previous four steps. This may seem time consuming, but it pays off in extended service life for the coupling.

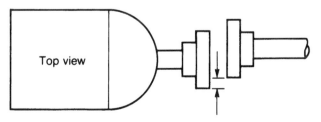

Figure 8-8.   Horizontal parallel.

Summary

Couplings are engineered to give good service life. However, most couplings are destroyed or have severely shortened service life by poor installation and maintenance practices. If the procedures outlined in this chapter are followed, the coupling will deliver the service it was intended to deliver when it was manufactured.

Chapter 9:
Sealing Fundamentals

Pumps, cylinders, and motors of fluid systems must have clearances for moving parts to avoid rubbing on one another. These clearances, however, allow the fluid to leak out (Fig. 9–1). To prevent this leakage, manufacturers have developed seals. Seals are devices for controlling the movement of fluids across a joint or opening in a vessel or assembly.

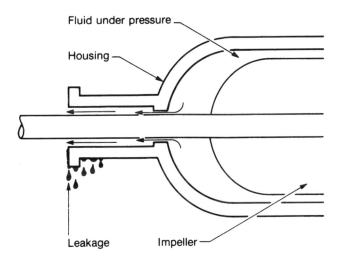

Figure 9-1. Leak.

Stuffing Box

Packings are a form of seal used where relative motion occurs. The stuffing box (Fig. 9–2) is used to control leakage at a point where a rod or shaft enters an enclosed space that's at pressure above or below that of the surrounding area.

The stuffing box has three basic parts:
1. packing chamber
2. packing rings
3. gland follower.

The packing is compressed by the gland follower and is forced against the bore of the box and the rotating shaft or rod. The packing must have the ability to deform in order to seal correctly. This type of packing is usually called compression packing. There must be frequent adjustments to compensate for wear. The packing must allow some leakage for lubricating purposes. This fluid lost as leakage helps dissipate generated heat and also prevents rapid wear. By not overtightening the packing, it will allow slight leakage.

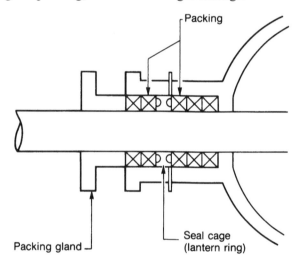

Figure 9-2.   Stuffing box assembly.

Packing Materials

Packing materials have four basic styles of construction: twisted packing, square braid, braid over braid, and interlocking braid.

Twisted packing (Fig. 9–3) is the most widely used and simply constructed. It is not, however, the strongest packing material. It's comprised of various materials, including cotton, lubricated with mineral oil and graphite. Its size is adjustable by merely removing strands.

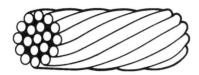

Figure 9-3. Twisted packing.

Square braid. The square braid (Fig. 9–4) is made of many materials (cotton, plastic, or leather, and may include metal wires of lead and copper) and usually has eight strands. It's usually grease or oil impregnated. It's very flexible and easily adjusted.

Figure 9-4. Square braid.

Braid over braid. The braid over braid (or jacket over jacket) (Fig. 9–5) type is made of a series of round tubes one over another. It's fabricated of various fibers and impregnated with lubricant. It may be braided over a lead core to help it hold its shape.

Figure 9-5. Braid over braid or jacket over jacket.

Interlocking braid. The interlocking braid (Fig. 9–6) is a combination of the braid over braid and the square braid. All the yarns are interlocking and have great resistance to unraveling. It's available in asbestos, cotton, plastic, and other fibers and is usually oil lubricated. It's the strongest of the packing materials.

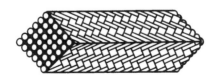

Figure 9-6. Interlocking braid.

Installation of Packing

Examination of the stuffing box reveals the reasons for correct installation procedures. The purpose of the multiple rings in a stuffing box is to break down the pressure of the fluid being sealed, so that when the pressure gets to the gland followers, it will be at zero psig. In practice, the bottom ring does most of the sealing. It's important to install it correctly. The common arrangement is the five packing rings and one lantern ring (or seal cage) (Fig. 9–2). The seal cage allows the introduction of a lubricating fluid between the packing and the shaft. It's possible to connect the discharge from the pump to the seal cage to introduce the lubricating fluid to the packing area. In abrasive conditions, or when pumping abrasive liquids, it is advisable to connect a line of cool, clean water to the seal cage.

When packing a stuffing box with a lantern ring, it's important to be sure that the seal cage is in line with the inlet port. As the packing is periodically adjusted for wear, the seal cage moves to the back of the stuffing box. The seal cage must be positioned so that it's always under the inlet port. It may be troublesome, but the life of the installation will be severely shortened if the seal cage is left out.

The following is a ten-step procedure for correctly installing packing.
1. Remove all old packing and clean the stuffing box. Make sure the inlet port to the seal cage is open and clean.
2. Cut the packing rings on the pump shaft or one of the same size (Fig. 9–7).

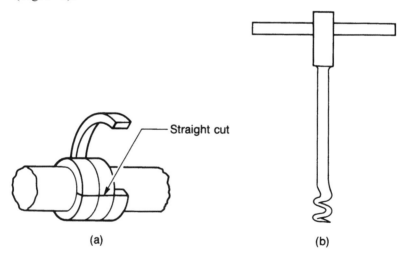

Figure 9-7.   (a) Cutting packing on a shaft, (b) tool to remove old packing.

3. Use the butt joint on all cuts except for valves and expansion joints (then use skive cut 45 degrees).
4. Put the first ring in, being careful to get it fully seated in the bottom. You may want to use an appropriate sized bushing or sleeve to assist.
5. Insert additional rings, being careful to stagger the joints for proper sealing and support.
6. Properly position the seal cage.
7. Finish installing the additional rings.
8. Install the gland follower. It should extend about 1/3 the depth of the packing.
9. Tighten the follower as you rotate the shaft. This prevents the follower from cocking and binding.
10. Open the valves and start the pump. Inspect for the proper amount of leakage. Make any necessary adjustments. Recheck in a few hours; additional adjustments may be required.

Mechanical Seals

In recent years, pump manufacturers have been installing a different type of seal on pumps called mechanical seals. These are much more expensive than the packing installed in the stuffing box installation, but they have no leakage. In some industries, leakage from stuffing boxes is unacceptable. The mechanical seal eliminates this problem.

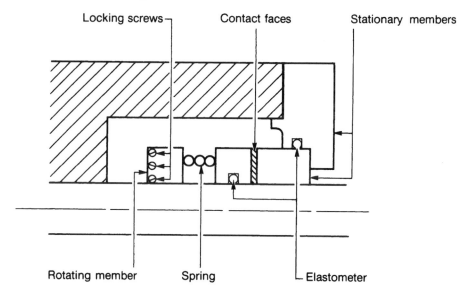

Figure 9-8. Inside mechanical seal.

The mechanical seal (Fig. 9–8) has five basic parts:
1. rotating member
2. stationary member
3. set screws
4. spring loaded collar
5. elastomer.

Types of Mechanical Seals

Mechanical seals fall into three distinct categories: inside seal, outside seal, and double seal.

Inside seals (Fig. 9–8) fit inside the stuffing box. The fluid pressure inside the stuffing box helps to hold the faces of the seal together. If the fluid pressure is excessive, a balanced seal may have to be used. A balanced seal has a cutaway on the inside of the seal to help balance out the pressure. The contact surfaces of the mechanical seal must never run dry. There must be some fluid in the pump; if there isn't, the friction will generate enough heat to destroy the seal.

Outside seals (Fig. 9–9) are located on the outside of the stuffing box. Since no rotating parts of the seal are located inside the stuffing box, this is a good seal to use when sealing corrosive and abrasive materials.

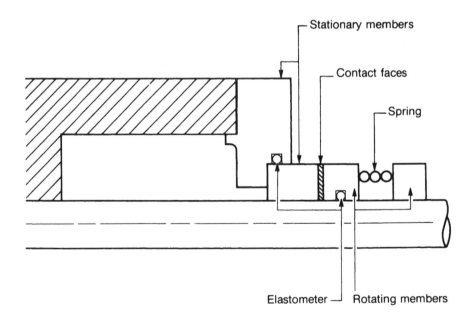

Figure 9-9.   Outside seal.

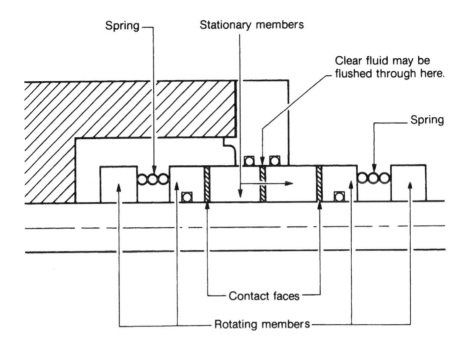

Figure 9-10.   Double seal.

Double mechanical seals (Fig. 9–10) are two single seals back to back. This seal is usually used for hazardous liquids. A clear fluid is circulated through the seals at higher than system pressure. This liquid would leak inward instead of outward, thereby assisting the seal to prevent leakage of the hazardous material. All three of the seals must have some lubrication of the contacting surfaces by a liquid. Running any of them dry will destroy them in a matter of seconds.

Installation of a Mechanical Seal

No one method or procedure can be outlined for installation of a mechanical seal. Some can be assembled in only one way and are very easy to install. Some may be installed only after inspecting the location and determining which procedure is correct. The outside is easy and obvious. The inside is harder because the equipment must be disassembled. The best method is to follow the procedure that's packed inside each seal by the manufacturer. Some manufacturers make seals that are preadjusted and merely have to be bolted on the pump.

Some installation points to watch are as follows.
- Check the shaft for runout and endplay (maximum of 0.005).
- Clean all burrs and sharp edges.
- Be sure there are no nicks or scratches in seal faces.
- Don't allow faces to make dry contact.
- Lubricate the seal faces with oil or the fluid to be sealed.
- Protect all static seals from sharp edges.
- Make sure the seal is surrounded by the liquid before startup.

O-ring Packing

The o-ring is a squeeze type packing made from synthetic rubber or similar materials. The most common shape is the circular cross section. The principle behind o-ring seals (Fig. 9–11) is called controlled deformation. A slight squeeze puts the o-ring into contact with both surfaces. The compression keeps the surfaces in contact. Additional deformation is caused by the pressure the fluid exerts on the o-ring.

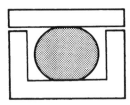

Figure 9-11.   O-ring.

The o-ring is usually used for static sealing and reciprocating motion. It can be used for oscillating and rotary motion if the speed is kept low. The o-ring usually fits into a rectangular groove that's 1 $1/2$ to 2 times the width of the o-ring. This allows the o-ring to slide and roll in the groove (Fig. 9–12). There are two reasons for this. First, it distributes wear on the o-ring. Second, it helps to lubricate the sliding surfaces. O-rings require about 10% initial preload to work properly. They are usually manufactured so that when they're installed, they have the necessary preload. There is presently no uniform sizing code in industry, and sizing varies from manufacturer to manufacturer.

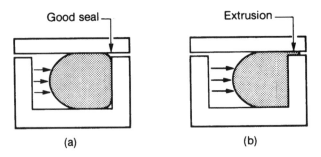

Figure 9-12.   O-ring deformation.

Lip packing

In addition to o-rings, manufacturers utilize a formed and molded packing to help eliminate leaks. One of the most common styles is lip-type packing. Lip packing must be installed so that the lips of the packing expand and collapse properly. If they're overtightened, they're improperly preloaded and become compression packings. A slight preload is required, but the sealing should occur as a result of the size and shape of the packing.

Types of Lip Packing

Lip type packings come in four basic types: cup packing, u-packing, flange packing, and v-shaped packing.

Cup packing (Fig. 9–13) is one of the most widely used types of packing. It's highly satisfactory for plunger end applications. It's an unbalanced packing since it has only one lip. The inside follower must only be snugged to prevent initial leaking. The clearance between the back plate and the cylinder walls must be very small. The clearance between the packing and the follower must be enough to allow the lips freedom to work.

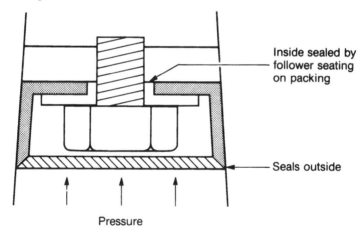

Figure 9-13. Cup packing.

U-packing (Fig. 9–14) is a balanced packing because it has two lips. It seals on the inside and outside surfaces. It must have some sort of support to prevent the lips from collapsing. For support, it usually uses some sort of material (flax, rubber, hemp, fiber, etc.) as a filler. It may even be supported by a metal ring (commonly called a pedestal ring). The ring must be such that it allows the lips freedom of movement to work properly.

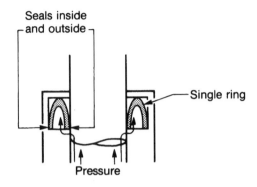

Figure 9-14.   U-packing.

Flange packing (Fig. 9–15) is the least used packing because it's good only for low pressure since it seals only on the inside surface. The outside surface must be sealed by the clamping force.

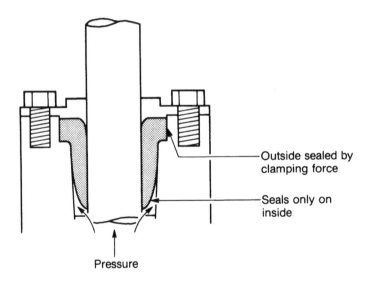

Figure 9-15.   Flange packing.

V-shaped packing (Fig. 9–16) is the most popular packing. It's effective on high or low pressure and on rotating or reciprocating applications. The inside angle is a standard 90 degree. It has the advantage that after it is worn slightly, it can be tightened to seal further. It's usually used in multiple packing. It has a support and adaptor ring at the top and the bottom. The support ring is usually metal, and the adaptor ring is made out of some other type of material.

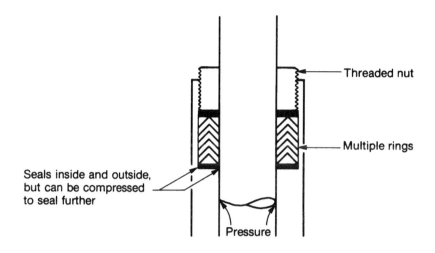

Figure 9-16. V-shaped packing.

Some points to consider when working with the lip-type packing are as follows.

1. Understand how the packing is to work. If installed incorrectly, it may trap fluid under pressure and thus wear the packing out much faster than it should.
2. Remove the old packing and examine it. Look for clues as to why it failed.
3. Look for worn surfaces at the end of the stroke or in reversal areas.
4. Check for dirt; clean the system if necessary.
5. Check the new packing for the correct size.
6. Make sure you have the correct adaptors, support rings, fillers, etc.
7. Look at the assembly and understand how it works.
8. Install correctly and do not overtighten.

Summary

A proper understanding of packing and sealing is important to prevent leakage. In some industries, leakage represents a loss of money, in others it is a hazard. No matter which problem faces the technician, there is some form of sealing device to solve the problem. It is up to the technician to decide which method is most suited to each case.

Chapter 10:
Fluid Power Fundamentals

A discussion of industrial power transmission systems wouldn't be complete without including fluid power systems. Fluid power systems are used for simple fluid transfer to advanced drive systems. As with any subject it's always best to start with the very basics and build to the more advanced systems. Every fluid power system must use a fluid medium. There are two very important terms in dealing with fluids, viscosity and density.

Viscosity

Viscosity is the fluid's resistance to flow. The higher the viscosity of a fluid the greater its resistance to flow. Conversely, the lower the viscosity the more

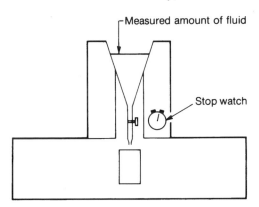

Figure 10-1. Saybolt Universal Seconds (SUS) test arrangement.

easily the fluid will flow. For example, cold molasses has a high viscosity and hot water has a low viscosity. As with any fluid, the colder it is, the higher its viscosity. This becomes important as the fluid power system undergoes temperature changes.

Measuring viscosity. There are several methods of measuring a fluid's viscosity. The most common is the Saybolt Universal Seconds (SUS) (Fig. 10–1). In this test, a certain amount of fluid must pass through a certain sized orifice. The time it takes to pass through (measured by a stopwatch) is the fluid's SUS rating. The tests are usually conducted at temperatures of 100°F and 210°F. Viscosity plays a very important part in the pump's ability to move the fluid, which will be discussed later.

Density

Density is a term that refers to the ratio of the fluid's weight to its volume. Density can be expressed in the following formula:

$$W = D \times V,$$

where W = weight
       D = density
       V = volume.

Note: The units of volume and density must be consistent. For example, if density is in lbs/cu ft, then volume must be in cubic feet and not in cubic inches.

Density is one way to evaluate the heaviness of a given material (see Table 10-1). For example, cork has a density of 15 lbs/cu ft, and water has a density of 62.4 lbs/cu ft. If a material is less dense than another, it will float or ride on top of the material with the higher density. This is why a cork will float in water.

Specific Gravity

Another method of comparing one material with another is specific gravity. Specific gravity is the ratio of the density of a substance compared to the density of fresh water. The formula is:

Specific Gravity = Density of substance ÷ Density of fresh water.

One point to keep in mind is that specific gravity applies only to liquids and solids. Gases change density when exposed to different pressures. Density and specific gravity can be determined for gases, but the pressure that the calculations were figured under must be stated.

Table 10-1

		Density Pounds Per Cu. Ft.	Density Pounds Per Cu. In.	Specific Gravity
Solids	Aluminum	166	0.096	2.67
	Asbestos	153	0.088	2.45
	Brass	532	0.308	8.55
	Brick	125	0.072	2.00
	Cement	90	0.052	1.45
	Concrete	145	0.084	2.43
	Copper	556	0.322	8.93
	Cork	15	0.008	0.24
	Glass	164	0.094	2.60
	Iron (cast)	450	0.260	7.21
	Iron (wrought)	485	0.287	7.78
	Lead	710	0.410	11.35
	Marble	170	0.098	2.73
	Mercury	848	0.491	13.60
	Steel	488	0.283	7.83
	Stone (granite)	160	0.093	2.78
	Timber (oak)	45	0.026	0.72
	Timber (soft pine)	25	0.014	0.40
Liquids	Mineral oil	55.6	0.032	0.89
	Water–oil emulsion	56.2	0.033	0.90
	Water–glycol solution	68.6	0.040	1.10
	Phosphate ester	68.6	0.040	1.10
	Silicone oil	64.8	0.038	1.04
	Castor oil	60.5	0.035	0.97
	Ethyl alcohol	49.4	0.029	0.794
	Ethylene–gycol	69.9	0.040	1.12
	Glycerol	78.6	0.045	1.26
	Linseed oil	58.8	0.034	0.944
	Mercury	849	0.491	13.6
	Mineral oil, SAE 10	56.7	0.033	0.91
	Olive oil	57.1	0.033	0.915
	Turpentine	54.3	0.031	0.872
	Water, fresh	62.35	0.036	1.0
	Water, salt	64.0	0.037	1.03

Pressure

Pressure is another term that must be considered in the study of fluid power. It is defined as force per unit of area. There are three ways that pressure can be created:

1. by the weight of a column of fluid,
2. by the force applied to a column of fluid, and
3. by resistance to flow.

The formula for **pressure created by the weight of a column of fluid** is:

Pressure = force ÷ area.

This calculation of pressure can be illustrated by examining a one-cubic-foot block of steel (representing the weight of a column of fluid) sitting on the floor (Fig. 10-2).

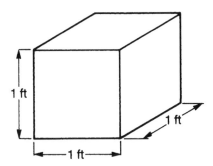

Figure 10-2.   Weight on a given area.

The density of steel is 488 lbs/cu ft. Since our block is 1 cubic ft, it weighs 488 lbs. Since the block is resting on its side, the weight of the block is acting on the floor on an area of 1 ft × 1 ft, or 1 square foot. The pressure (P) then becomes:

P = 488 pounds ÷ 1 square foot

or, if the conversion is made to square inches (Fig. 10–3), it becomes:

P = 488 pounds ÷ 144 square inches = 3.39 lbs/sq in (psi).

The unit psi is the most commonly used unit in fluid power; it means "pounds per square inch."

All substances, including fluids, exert a force similar to the steel block. With fluids, it's possible to measure the pressure in any given point in the height of the column. The **pressure exerted by a column of fluid** can be determined if the height of the column and the specific gravity (sp gr) of the fluid are known. Using the constant for determining static pressure in water (0.433 psi/ft), the formula is:

P = 0.433 psi/ft × sp gr × height (of the column of fluid in feet).

For example: Determine the pressure at the bottom of a tank of mineral oil, SAE 10, that is 25 feet high. (Find the specific gravity for mineral oil, SAE 10, from Table 10–1).

P = 0.433 × 0.91 × 25 ft.

P = 9.85 psi.

The concept of pressure is important to the understanding of how fluid power systems function. One critical concept of pressure is stated in Pascal's law:

Pressure on a confined fluid is transmitted undiminished and in all directions, and acts with equal force on equal areas and at right angles to them.

This principle is best illustrated by a closed container that has four plungers (Fig. 10–3).

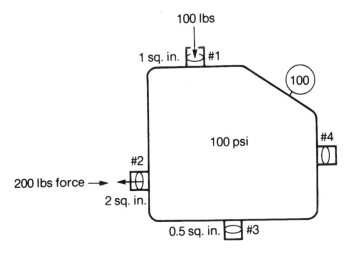

Figure 10-3. How force on a confined fluid creates pressure.

The force is applied to plunger #1 (a force of 100 lbs). Plunger # 1 has an area of 1 sq in. Plunger #2 has an area of 2 sq in., and plunger #3 has an area of 0.5 sq in. Plunger #1 has applied to it a force of 200 lbs.

P = force ÷ area, therefore

F = P × A.

For plunger #1,

P = 100/1 (or 100 psi).

The 100 psi is the pressure inside the closed container. The force on plunger #2 is

F = 100 psi × 2 sq in.,
F = 200 lbs.

The force on plunger #3 is

F = 100 psi × 0.5 sq in.,
F = 50 psi.

Resistance to flow also creates pressure. Whenever flow is restricted, the pressure increases. The fluid always flows from a point of high pressure to a point of lower pressure, and the fluid always flows through the path of least resistance. In fluid power circuits there are two types of flow paths: series and parallel (Fig. 10–4).

In series flow paths, the pressures add with subsequent restrictors (Fig. 10–5).

In parallel flow paths the flow takes the path of least resistance (Fig. 10–6).

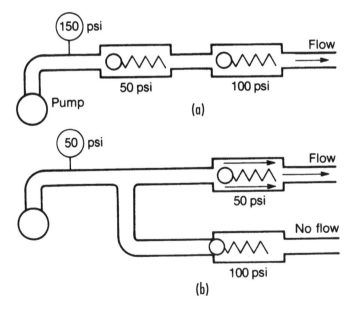

Figure 10-4.   Series and parallel flow paths.

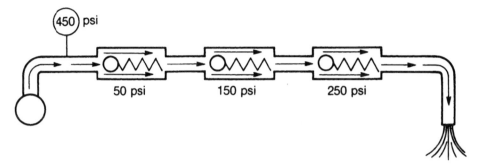

Figure 10-5.   Series flow path.

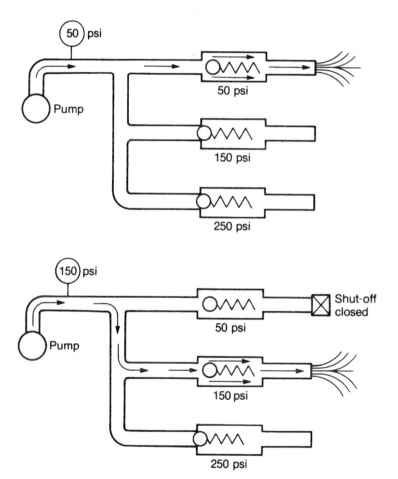

Figure 10-6.   Parallel flow paths.

A device that's used to control flow or create pressure is called an orifice. The orifice may be a restricted passage in a pipe or a valve. The amount of flow through an orifice is determined by three variables:

1. size of the orifice,
2. viscosity of the fluid, and
3. pressure drop.

Pressure Scales

One final area to consider in fluid power systems is pressure scales, which measure the pressure a column of fluid exerts at the bottom of a column. Because the atmosphere is a fluid, it exerts a pressure at the surface of the earth. At sea level that pressure is 14.7 psia (pounds per square inch absolute). The *psia scale* starts at a perfect vacuum (0 psia); atmospheric pressure is equal to 14.7 on this scale.

Another scale is the gauge scale. A gauge scale ignores atmospheric pressure, which would be 0 psig (pounds per square inch gauge). Table 10–2 gives the conversions for popular pressure scales. A conversion formula for the psia to psig scales is as follows:

psig + 14.7 = psia
psia – 14.7 = psig.

Table 10-2

Atmospheric Pressure at Sea Level	Psia Scale 14.7	Psig Scale 0	Inches of Mercury 29.92	Feet of Water 34
2 Atmospheres	29.4	14.7	60 inches	74 feet
3 Atmospheres	44.1	29.4	90 inches	111 feet

Pump Inlet

Atmospheric pressure becomes very important when considering the beginning of a fluid power system—the pump inlet. The fluid is not sucked into the inlet of a pump, as is often thought. Atmospheric pressure acting on the surface of the fluid forces the fluid into the pump inlet, which is a place of lower pressure. This means that there will be flow from an area of higher pressure (the reservoir) to an area of lower pressure (the pump inlet) (Fig. 10–7).

Cavitation. If it were possible to create a perfect vacuum at the inlet of a pump, you could lift a column of fluid equal to 14.7 psia. But this is impossible. Even if it were possible, there would be a serious problem. There is

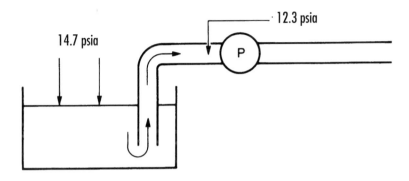

Figure 10-7.   Flow from an area of higher pressure to an area of lower pressure.

dissolved air in all fluids, and at different pressures the dissolved air comes out of the fluid. At any pressure less than 12.2 psia, the dissolved air will bubble out of petroleum oil. When the air bubbles are carried to the outlet of the pump, they are exposed to pressures greater than atmospheric pressure. Under this increased pressure, they implode back into the fluid (Fig. 10–8). This implosion will actually be severe enough to remove metal from the pump, thus causing deterioration of the pump. Unless the problem is corrected, rapid failure of the pump can be expected. The condition just described is called cavitation. Cavitation is noted by loud operating noises. In fact, it usually sounds as if the pump has gravel in it. Once the loud noise is heard, every effort should be taken to correct the condition before the pump is destroyed.

Inlet Air Leak. One condition that is often confused with cavitation is an inlet air leak. The inlet in some way allows the passage of some air from the atmosphere into the oil before it enters the pump (Fig. 10–9). Under the pres-

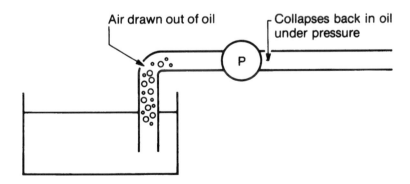

Figure 10-8.   Cavitation.

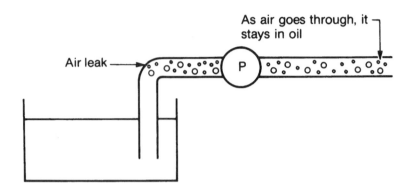

Figure 10-9.   Flow from an area of higher pressure to an area of lower pressure.

sure on the outlet side of the pump, the air is dissolved into the oil, again resulting in the increased noise levels. The noise is caused by the violent implosion of the air bubbles on the pressure side of the pump. The way to tell the difference between cavitation and an inlet air leak is to look in the reservoir. If it's cavitation, the oil will appear normal in color. If it's an inlet air leak, the air trapped under high pressure will bubble out in the reservoir. This leaves the oil with a foam on top or a milky color in the tank. Inlet air leaks are not as damaging as cavitation; however, over a long period of time, the results are the same. Both conditions should be corrected as soon as practical when they are detected.

Hydraulics and Pneumatics

Beginning the study of fluid power systems is like coming to a "Y" in a road. The systems branch off into two broad categories, hydraulics and pneumatics. The next two chapters will cover these systems.

Chapter 11:
Hydraulic Systems

All hydraulic systems are comprised of basically the same components. The following material will present a broad overview of the components and how they function in the system.

Reservoir

All hydraulic systems begin with the reservoir (Fig. 11–1), which has several functions:

1. to store the fluid,
2. to allow air to separate from the fluid,
3. to allow contaminants to settle out of the fluid, and
4. to allow for temperature control of the fluid.

The reservoir (Fig. 11–2) holds the fluid prior to its entry into the system through the pump. It's usually made of steel plates welded together. The tank will normally have a drain at the bottom to allow the fluid to be periodically changed. There's usually a removable endplate that can be used for access to clean the tank. The tank is also commonly provided with an external sight glass to check the fluid level. The reservoir is equipped with a breather (unless the reservoir is pressurized) to allow the atmosphere to equalize the pressure inside the tank whether it's empty or full.

Inside the reservoir there's usually a baffle plate. The baffle plate prevents the returning oil from being drawn directly back to the inlet and sent back into the system. The baffle plate slows down the oil, and allows for any contaminants to

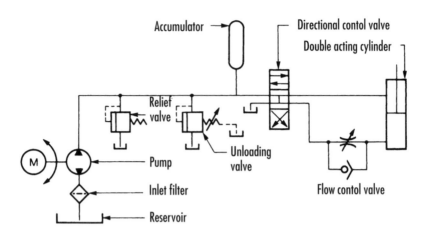

Figure 11-1. The location of the reservoir in a hydraulic system.

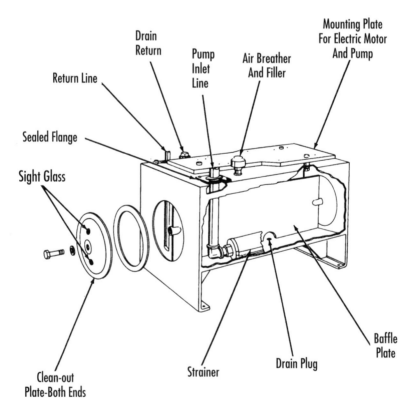

Figure 11-2. Typical hydraulic reservoir. *(Courtesy of Sperry-Vickers.)*

settle to the bottom of the tank. This also helps to remove any entrapped air from the oil. By making the oil swirl around the tank, the oil is cooled before going back into the system.

Hydraulic systems that have a problem with heat are usually equipped with a heat exchanger (Fig. 11–3). This is usually a series of cells in the bottom of the reservoir that have cold water (or some other cooling medium) circulated through them to remove the heat from the fluid. In some rare cases, there are examples of heaters in the tank to warm the oil before it enters the system. This is usually found only in very cold climates where the viscosity of the oil needs to be lowered before it enters the pump.

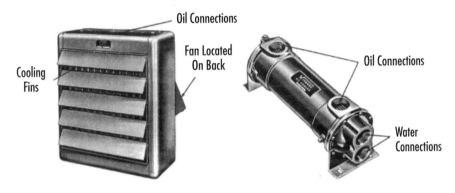

Figure 11-3.   Heat exchangers (coolers). *(Courtesy of Sperry-Vickers.)*

Filters

The intake line to the pump may be equipped with a filter (Fig. 11–4) to prevent the pump from drawing contaminants into the system. This is one of the most common locations of the filter or strainer (a strainer is a coarse filter). Filters are rated in microns (0.000039 inch). The lower the micron rating of the filter, the smaller the particle it will remove. As the filter removes contaminants from the fluid, it begins to allow less and less fluid to pass through the filter element. Finally, it won't allow enough flow for the pump to work properly. If it's not replaced before this time, the pump will begin to cavitate. This is an important reason for the filter to be serviced on a regular schedule.

Figure 11-4.
Typical inlet filter.
(Courtesy of Sperry-Vickers.)

Filters are rated on two systems—the nominal rating and the absolute rating. The nominal rating is the size of particle that the filter will stop most of the time. For example, a filter with a nominal rating of 30 microns will stop most particles 30 microns or larger. The absolute rating is the size of the smallest particle that can't pass through the filter. For example, a filter with an absolute rating of 25 microns will stop all particles of the 25-micron size or larger (unless the contaminant particles are well rounded or long thin objects that may snake their way through the filter).

Other types of filters may be found in a hydraulic system, and they will be considered as their location in the system comes along.

The Pump

The fluid passes through the filter and next enters the pump. Pumps can be classified as nonpositive displacement or positive displacement. Nonpositive displacement pumps are usually used in fluid transfer systems and aren't common in hydraulic systems. The nonpositive displacement pumps don't discharge a certain volume for each revolution of the pump. A positive displacement pump produces a given flow at a given speed. Positive displacement pumps are divided into three basic types (Fig. 11–5): vane, gear, and piston. All three types of pumps work on the principle of expanding and decreasing volume.

Vane pumps consist of three basic parts: the *vanes,* the *rotor,* and the *housing.* As the rotor turns, the vanes extend out and contact the housing. The vanes

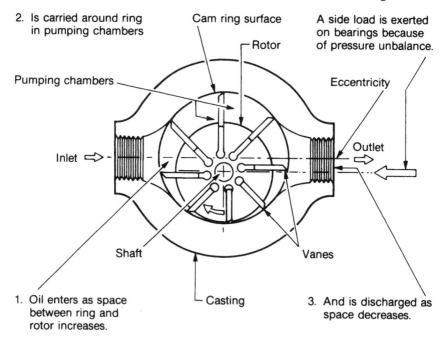

Figure 11-5a.   Typical vane pump. *(Courtesy of Sperry-Vickers.)*

may be spring loaded or may depend on the centrifugal force of the turning rotor to hold them out against the cam ring during startup.

After the pump develops flow, the downstream pressure is used to hold the vanes against the cam ring. The chamber created by the vanes extending against the cam ring varies in size as the unit is rotated. The chamber increases in size as it approaches the inlet and decreases in size as it approaches the outlet. This decreasing chamber forces the fluid out of the chamber to the outlet.

Some vane pumps have adjustable volume. This style of pump allows you to move the rotor assembly to increase or decrease the chamber size. This, then, adjusts the amount of fluid that's forced out the discharge of the pump.

There are also *double vane* pumps. These pumps are actually two different pumps in the same housing. They are driven by the same shaft. The pumps usually come in different sizes: one stage is used for low volume and the other is used for high volume. This allows the designer some versatility in setting speeds of system components.

Gear pumps are two gears that are driven together. As the gears pass the inlet, they pick up fluid that's trapped between the gear and the housing as the gear continues to rotate. The gear rotates to the outlet, where the trapped fluid is forced out of the outlet by the meshing of the two gears. The output of the gear pump can't be adjusted as can the vane pump. The only way to change the

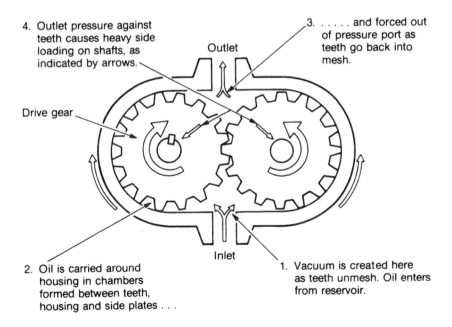

Figure 11-5b.   Typical gear pump. *(Courtesy of Sperry-Vickers.)*

output is to speed up the prime mover driving the pump. The size of the chambers can't be varied so the output will be directly proportional to the speed at which the pump is driven.

Piston pumps consist of a series of cylinders moving in and out of chambers. The cylinders retract as they approach the inlet, allowing the fluid to fill the cylinder chamber. As they approach the outlet, the cylinder moves back in, forcing the fluid out of the cylinder. There are several types of piston pumps (bent, axis, and radial) but the principles are the same. The volumetric output of the pumps can be varied by increasing or decreasing the stroke of the piston.

Pump Flow and Pressure

There is one important point to remember about all pumps: pumps develop flow, not pressure. The pump displaces fluid, and if the outlet were left open, the pump would displace fluid under almost zero pressure. The restriction in the system or its resistance to flow is what develops the pressure. If the outlet of the pump is completely sealed, the pressure would theoretically increase till the pump destroyed itself.

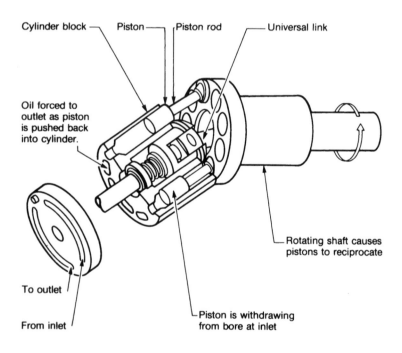

Figure 11-5c.   Typical piston pump. *(Courtesy of Sperry-Vickers.)*

The problem of pressure building is prevented in the system by a *pressure relief valve* (Fig. 11–6). This valve is usually installed immediately after the pump. Its purpose is to allow the system pressure to build to a certain level; and after the pressure reaches that level, the valve will dump the fluid to a tank. The valve is usually spring loaded, with a screw adjustment. As the screw is tightened, it compresses the spring, requiring higher pressure to open the valve. The problem with a relief valve is that when fluid is dumping to the tank through it, it is doing so under pressure, and the stored energy is converted to heat. This heat is transferred to the fluid and then must be dissipated in the tank. A solution to this problem is an accumulator (Fig. 11–7).

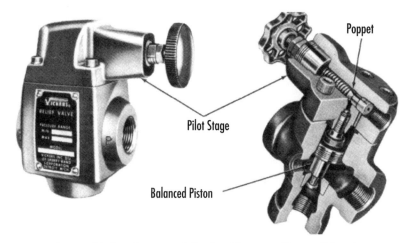

Figure 11-6.   Pressure relief valve. *(Courtesy of Sperry-Vickers.)*

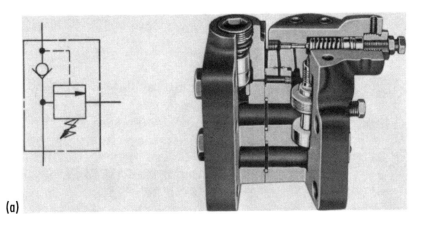

(a)

Figure 11-7.   (a) Unloading valve. *(Courtesy of Sperry-Vickers.)*

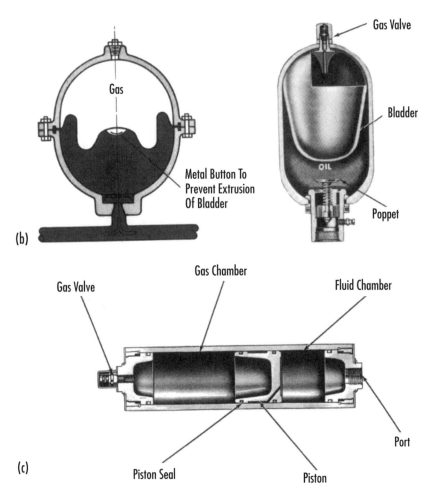

Figure 11-7. (b) Diaphragm accumulator, (c) piston accumulator. *(Courtesy of Sperry-Vickers.)*

The *accumulator* is to the hydraulic system what the battery is to an electrical system. The accumulator is a storage unit that holds a given volume of fluid under pressure. When the system requires flow, the fluid stored in the accumulator provides it. The pump runs the entire time, but its flow is diverted to the tank across an *unloading valve*. When the system pressure lowers to a given point, the unloading valve closes and flow is provided to the system until a certain pressure is reached and the accumulator is recharged. When these conditions are met, a pilot line to the unloading valve opens the valve, dumping the pump flow to the tank. The advantage of the unloading valve over the relief valve is that it dumps under low pressure, which means less heat will be generated. This protects the system components from heat buildup that would be likely with just a relief valve.

The *check valve* (Fig. 11–8) allows flow in one direction and blocks flow in the other direction. It's easier to picture if you visualize the ball pushing into the v-shaped holder of the valve, blocking the flow. Then when the flow is reversed, the ball is pushed off its seat allowing the flow to pass by the ball.

The *directional control valve* (d.c.v.) (Fig. 11–9) is the next valve in the circuit. It's used to control the direction of the flow to the actuator. The most common directional control valves are the four-way directional control valves. They come in the 2-position or the 3-position valve. The two end envelopes in the d.c.v. are used to change the direction of the flow. The middle envelope is called the center.

There are four basic types of center conditions in a d.c.v., each with its own advantage. They are: open, tandem, closed, and float.

Open center. The open center allows the flow to return to the tank under low pressure without an unloading valve. The disadvantage of the open center is that once it's centered, the pump can't be used to power any

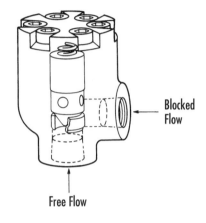

Figure 11-8. Right angle check valve. *(Courtesy of Sperry-Vickers.)*

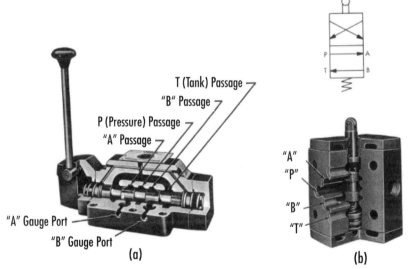

Figure 11-9. Directional control valves: (a) manual 4-way d.c.v., (b) mechanically operated d.c.v. *(Courtesy of Sperry-Vickers.)*

other actuator. For this reason, it is typically found in a circuit that activates only one actuator.

Closed center. The closed center blocks all passages in the valve. This center can be used in circuits with more than one actuator. The actuators may act independently of each other in this system. The disadvantage of this type of center is that the pump flow must be diverted by other means (relief valve, unloading valve). This valve also allows for some leakage around the spool, which may cause an actuator without a load on it to creep.

Tandem center. Tandem center valves are used to unload the pump to the tank and at the same time block any flow to the actuator. The problem with this type of center is that the passages are so small, there's a significant pressure drop across the valve, which means generated heat. To compensate for this, some manufacturers enlarge the lands on the spool for the pressure and tank ports. This decreases the size of the ports to the actuator, which restricts the flow and results in slower operation, but does keep the center cooler.

Float center. The float center blocks the pressure port and vents the actuator lines to the tank. This allows the actuator to drift if necessary. The disadvantage to this type of valve is that the actuator cannot be stopped or held in any position. It does, however, eliminate any pressure buildup across the lands on the spool.

Actuating the Directional Control Valve. There are several ways that a directional control valve can be actuated. One of the most common methods is with the electric solenoid. It uses an electrical current fed through a coil in the valve to set up a magnetic field to shift the spool (Fig. 11–10). Another common way is with a pilot-operated d.c.v. These valves use a pressure from another part of the system (or from an external source) to shift the spool (Fig. 11–11).

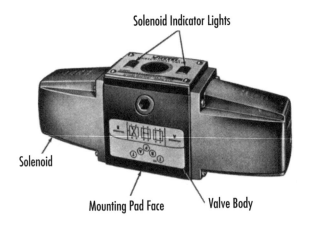

Solenoid Indicator Lights

Solenoid

Mounting Pad Face   Valve Body

Figure 11-10. Solenoid-operated directional control valve. *(Courtesy of Sperry-Vickers.)*

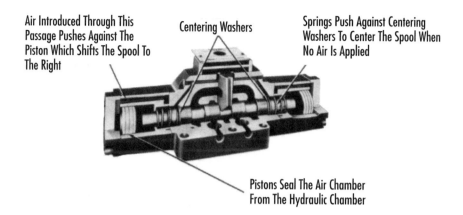

Air Introduced Through This Passage Pushes Against The Piston Which Shifts The Spool To The Right

Centering Washers

Springs Push Against Centering Washers To Center The Spool When No Air Is Applied

Pistons Seal The Air Chamber From The Hydraulic Chamber

Figure 11-11.   Pilot-operated directional control valve. *(Courtesy of Sperry-Vickers.)*

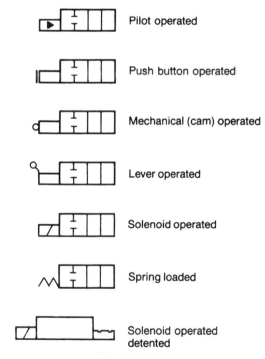

Pilot operated

Push button operated

Mechanical (cam) operated

Lever operated

Solenoid operated

Spring loaded

Solenoid operated detented

Figure 11-12.   Symbols of directional control valve (d.c.v.) actuators.

The other ways are *manual,* by using a foot pedal, a hand operated control, a cam operated switch, or some type of push button (Fig. 11–12). They all have their purpose in industry. Their placement in the system is usually chosen by the original equipment manufacturer.

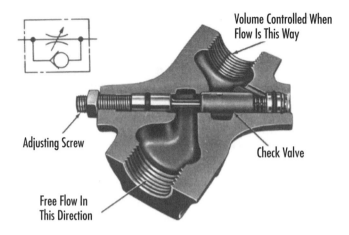

Figure 11-13.   Flow control valve with bypass. *(Courtesy of Sperry-Vickers.)*

Flow Control Valves. The next valve in the line is the flow control valve (Fig. 11–13). This valve controls the flow, so it will affect the speed of the actuator. The valve is an orifice, which may or may not be adjustable, with a check valve in parallel with it. The flow is controlled in one direction and is allowed to bypass the valve in the other direction. This valve can be used in two ways in a circuit. It can either meter in or meter out. The meter in controls the flow into the actuator and allows free flow out of the actuator. The meter out allows full flow into the actuator, but restricts the flow out of the actuator.

Actuator

The final item in a typical hydraulic circuit is the actuator. The actuator can be either a cylinder or a motor.

Hydraulic cylinder actuators. There are three types of hydraulic cylinders: single acting, double acting, and double rod (Fig. 11–14).

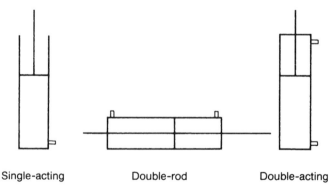

Figure 11-14.   Three types of hydraulic cylinders.

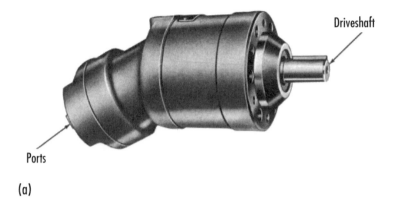

Driveshaft

Ports

(a)

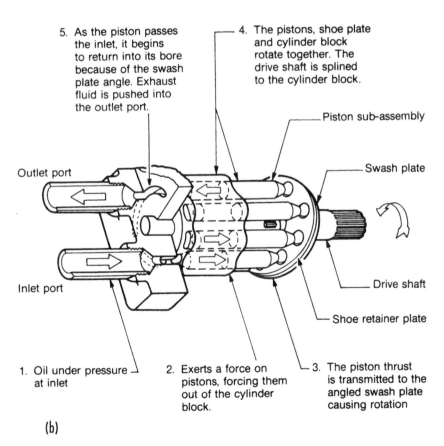

5. As the piston passes the inlet, it begins to return into its bore because of the swash plate angle. Exhaust fluid is pushed into the outlet port.

4. The pistons, shoe plate and cylinder block rotate together. The drive shaft is splined to the cylinder block.

Piston sub-assembly

Swash plate

Outlet port

Inlet port

Drive shaft

Shoe retainer plate

1. Oil under pressure at inlet

2. Exerts a force on pistons, forcing them out of the cylinder block.

3. The piston thrust is transmitted to the angled swash plate causing rotation

(b)

Figure 11-15 (a-c).   Vane motor. *(Courtesy of Sperry-Vickers.)*

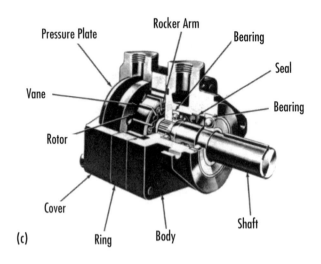

Pressure Plate
Rocker Arm
Bearing
Seal
Vane
Bearing
Rotor
Cover
Ring
Body
Shaft
(c)

Figure 11-15 (a-c).   Vane motor. *(Courtesy of Sperry-Vickers.)*

The *single acting* cylinder applies force only in one direction. It must be retracted by another force, whether spring, gravity, or the load. The *double acting* cylinder extends or retracts with force. The cylinder extends with more force than it will retract, because the rod end of the cylinder piston has less area for the pressure to act upon (because of the cylinder rod). The *double rod* cylinder has two rods so it extends and retracts with equal force.

Hydraulic motor actuators. Hydraulic motors can be of two types: *reversible* or *nonreversible* (Fig. 11–15).

The motors may also be classified by the driven element: vane, gear, and piston. The motor works in the reverse of the pump. The fluid tries to get from an area of high pressure (inlet) to an area of low pressure (outlet). In doing so, the motor shaft is turned. The greater the flow coming into the motor, the faster it will turn.

Summary

In this brief overview of the basic hydraulic system, we have considered the primary system components. There are many other, newer styles of valves and devices that will continually be changed and updated to improve the performance of the system. The increasing technology in hydraulics makes it a field that offers limitless potential for advancement. Along with that comes the challenge to learn.

Chapter 12:
Pneumatic Systems

Introduction

Man has harnessed the power of the wind to power many devices. In the last century, air was first used as a power transmission medium. A brief comparison of pneumatic and hydraulic systems is given below.

Pneumatic System	Hydraulic System
Uses air under pressure.	Uses liquid under pressure.
Is a low power system.	Is a high power system.
Has a compressible transmitting medium.	Has an incompressible transmitting medium.
Is a low pressure system (90 psi).	Is a high pressure system (10,000+ psi).
Has lighter and less expensive components.	Has heavier and more expensive components.
Leaks are clean.	Leaks can create environmental and housekeeping problems.
Uses air, which is cheap.	Uses hydraulic fluid, which is expensive.

Pneumatic systems have their place in low power applications. Before describing the components of pneumatic systems, it is important to consider some facts about air, temperature, humidity, and pressure.

Air is generally composed of 21% oxygen, 78% nitrogen, and 1% inert gases. The atmosphere at any time can contain 4% water vapor. Since gas molecules are at a distance from each other they can be compressed. The air always assumes the shape of its containers and exerts a pressure at sea level of 14.7 psia.

The quality of air that is most problematic for pneumatic systems is humidity. Absolute humidity is the amount of water vapor that the air can carry. This is directly affected by the temperature of the air. Relative humidity is the amount of water vapor carried by a volume of air compared to the amount of water vapor that it could carry (expressed as a percentage). As the temperature of the air increases, the amount of water vapor that it can hold increases. The amount of water vapor the air carries doubles for every 20 degree temperature rise. When the water vapor reaches 100% saturation, the vapor is released as a liquid.

Dew point is the temperature at which the air becomes saturated with water vapor. This is important to pneumatic systems, for when warm compressed air travels through the branch lines it cools. As it drops below the dew point, the water condenses in the lines. The water then damages the air lines (by rust) and the pneumatic operating devices. An important consideration is that when a gas is compressed, its temperature rises. If you release it from compression (or lower the pressure), it cools.

The flow in a pneumatic system is measured in cubic feet per minute (cfm).

1 cfm = 7.48 gpm

A rule to remember in a pneumatic system is that ·flow causes movement, pressure causes force. To solve for horsepower in a pneumatic system:

HP = (Flow [cfm]) × psi) ÷ 12,280

The result is the horsepower.

Building a Pneumatic System

The following is a discussion of the components that may be found in a typical pneumatic system.

Compressor. Pneumatic systems must have a prime mover, that is, some sort of device to power the compressor. This will typically be an electric motor or fuel-driven engine. The compressor is the start of the pneumatic system. It takes the power from the prime mover and converts it to flow against pressure. Compressors can be classified as either positive displacement or nonpositive displacement. Nonpositive displacement compressors are usually blowers with high volume and low pressure. Most pneumatic systems use positive displacement compressors. The three main types of positive displacement compressors are the piston, diaphragm, and vane compressors (Fig. 12–1).

Inlet Filter. The compressor is like a pump; it has an inlet and an outlet. The inlet of the compressor has to be filtered to remove dirt and other contaminants. The inlet filter (Fig. 12–2) may be of two types: the *wet* or the *dry.*

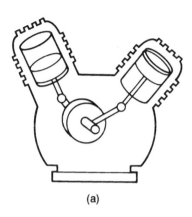 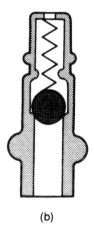

(a)   (b)

Figure 12-1.   (a) Compressor; (b) relief valve to prevent excessive pressure buildup in a compressor.

The dry is usually a cartridge filter that can be disposed of when it gets dirty. Some dry inlet filters are made to be cleaned, then dried, and reused. The wet filters are usually composed of a mesh and a shallow oil reservoir. The air is drawn through the reservoir, and the dust and dirt are dampened by the oil and removed by the filter before the air gets to the compressor.

The inlet should always be located in a cool dry area. The cool air molecules make the compressor more efficient, because cool air molecules are closer together. Care should be taken to ensure that no combustible fumes are drawn into the compressor.

Intercooler. By staging a compressor, a boost in the pressure can be achieved. Staging is a procedure in which one stage of the compressor is fed into the second stage. The

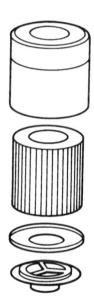

Figure 12-2.   Inlet filter.

air is already compressed, coming from the first stage, and the second stage compresses it and further increases the pressure. The problem is that when the air is compressed, it's hot coming from the first stage. To cool the air before it gets to the second stage, you may need an intercooler (Fig. 12-3).

This device cools the air in between stages. By doing this, it makes the second stage more efficient by letting it compress cooler air. The intercooler may

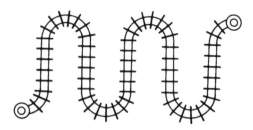

Figure 12-3.   Intercooler. The intercooler may be nothing more than finned tubing.

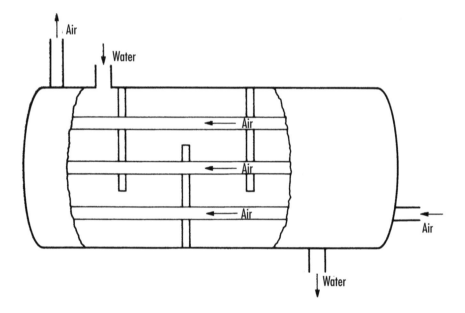

Figure 12-4.   Water-cooled aftercooler.

also remove some condensed water vapor from the air. There are two basic types of intercoolers: air-cooled and water-cooled. The air-cooled may be circulating the compressed air through lengths of finned tubing. The water-cooled usually circulates the compressed air through a tank containing water lines, through which cooled water is circulated. The water-cooled is the most efficient, and is usually equipped with drains to remove condensation.

Aftercooler. After the compressed air leaves the compressor it may be circulated through another cooler called an aftercooler (Fig. 12–4). The aftercoolers are larger than the intercoolers, because they have the air circulating through at a higher pressure. The aftercoolers are usually a water type because they are more efficient than the air cooled type. The aftercooler may have a drain to remove any condensation or the air may pass through a *separator* (Fig. 12–5) immediately after leaving the aftercooler.

The dew point of the compressed air becomes critical at this point. If the moisture isn't removed, as the air is cooled further downstream more moisture may condense and damage (usually by corrosion) the downstream components.

There is a separator that is usually found after the aftercooler. It removes some moisture by centrifugal force, and it will

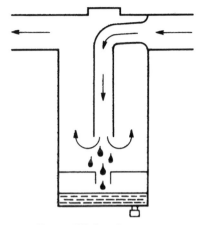

Figure 12-5.   Separator.

also remove any oil that's in the air from the compressor. It usually has a manual or automatic drain on it to prevent it from getting too full.

Refrigeration Dryer. Another device that may be found is a refrigeration dryer (Fig. 12–6). This uses a gas to super-cool (never below 35°F) the air to get all possible moisture condensed out of the air.

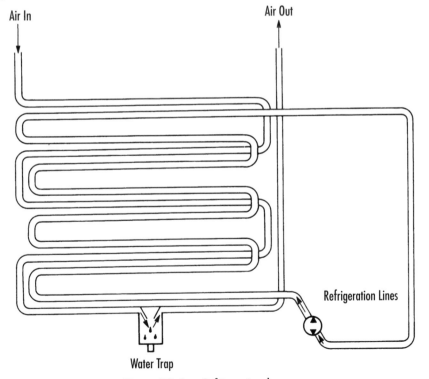

Figure 12-6.   Refrigeration dryer.

Chemical Dryer. If extremely clean and dry air is required for the system, a *chemical dryer* (Fig. 12–7) may be found next in the line. There are basically two types of chemical dryers: deliquescent and nondeliquescent. The deliquescent uses a chemical that absorbs the water vapor from the air. As the chemical does so, it melts, forming a compound that must be periodically removed. The dryer must also be periodically refilled with the chemical.

The nondeliquescent (or absorption) dryer uses a chemical that traps the water vapor, and it must be periodically dried out for reuse. Some styles use electric elements in the dryer to heat the chemical to remove the water vapor. Others use hot air blown through the dryer to remove the moisture. These are usually a two-unit type so that one can be drying out while the other is drying the air.

Receiver. Next the air is ready to go to the receiver (Fig. 12–8). The receiver is like an accumulator. It stores compressed air under pressure and serves three purposes:

1. dissipates heat,
2. collects moisture as the air cools, and
3. dampens the compressor pulsations and makes the flow smoother and quieter.

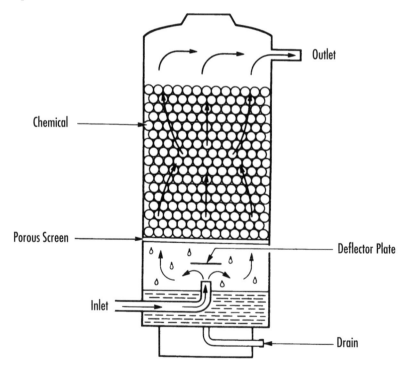

Figure 12-7. Chemical dryer.

Filters. The next component in a pneumatic system is the filter (Fig. 12–9). Filters remove the contaminants in a system before they get to the downstream components. There are basically two types of contaminants in a pneumatic system.

1. Those generated by the system: rust particles, pipe compound, grit, oil, or water sludge.
2. Those from an outside source: rivets, small nails, metal chips, fine airborne particles, or chemical fumes that the compressor may have sucked into the system.

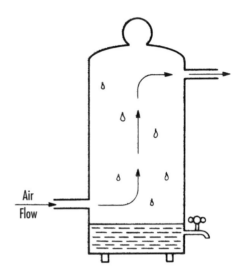

Figure 12-8.   Receiver.

Some of the contaminants, such as rust (formed by condensation in the lines), form a sludge that will damage the downstream components. This can also restrict air flow, or possibly damage a finished product to which air is being applied (paint, etc.).

Filters are rated in microns (0.000039 inch). They're given either a nominal rating or an absolute rating. The nominal rated filter will remove the largest percentage of the stated micron size. The absolute rated filter is supposed to remove 100% of its stated size. In actuality, the filter removes only about 98%; the other 2% are long, slim, well-rounded particles that are not easily trapped.

Types of Filters. Filter elements are made of either cloth, felt, or of wire mesh construction. Cloth filters have high filtration qualities and a low pressure drop. They're usually rated at 5 microns or greater. They can load with water and sludge and deteriorate in the system.

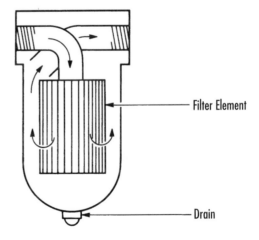

Figure 12-9.   Filter

Wire mesh filters can be cleaned. They're rated at 40 microns and above. They can clog and create a substantial pressure drop. They can also be damaged very easily during cleaning. Wire mesh filters should be used on line sizes of 2 inches to $1/4$ inch. If used on larger lines, they aren't capable of allowing the necessary air flow. When the filters get dirty, they can create a substantial pressure drop, with decreased flow, because there is no bypass of the filter. The filter can actually stop all flow.

There are also absorption filters designed to collect vapors other than water vapor. These are usually some type of carbon powder or granular chemicals. They're usually rated in the 0.5 (and above) micron range.

Regulator. The next component in the pneumatic system is the regulator (Fig. 12–10a), which controls the downstream pressure. There are several basic types of regulators. The *diaphragm type* uses a flexible diaphragm to move the valve. As the downstream pressure increases, the diaphragm flexes and closes the valve, not allowing any more flow to pass through. When the pressure decreases, the valve opens and allows flow to continue downstream.

The *externally controlled type* uses a pilot device downstream to regulate the valve to control the downstream pressure. Some types of regulators have built-in relief valves to relieve pressure. This is a safety factor when the high pressure could damage downstream components. These valves shouldn't take the place of the standard relief valve found in the vicinity of the compressor.

Lubricator. The lubricator (Fig. 12–10b) is found next in the system. An air lubricator injects oil into the air stream to lubricate the internal workings of pneumatic devices. It usually stores lubricant and injects it into the air stream by

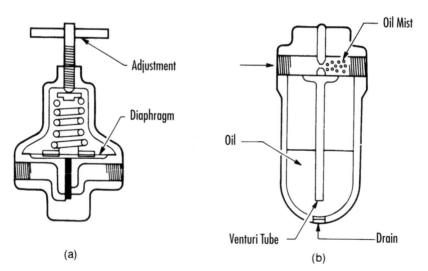

(a)   (b)

Figure 12-10. (a) Regulator, (b) lubricator.

the venturi effect. The air then carries minute droplets of oil downstream. Problems could develop at bends in the lines. The bends cause the oil to accumulate and to travel as a liquid. This is why the lubricator should be installed as close to the pneumatic device as possible.

Another point to consider is that the lubricator can act as a check valve when installed in reverse. It'll restrict flow in the returning line. It makes a big difference how the lubricator is installed in lines that must carry return flow. The regulator has a pressure drop of 2 to 5 psi.

To ensure proper lubrication, it is advisable to use an SAE 10 lightweight oil. Light oils are easier to atomize. The compatibility with the lubricator is a factor to watch. Some oils have chemical reactions with the plastic bowls on the lubricator.

The FRL System. Some pneumatic systems have what is known as an FRL system. This is a combination unit of a filter, regulator, and lubricator. The components must be installed in this order to function correctly. The contaminants must be removed, the pressure regulated, then the oil added. If the oil is added first, it would be removed in the filter.

Directional Control Valve. The next component in the system is the directional control valve. Directional control valves are used to direct or prevent flow through selected passages. There are several styles of directional control valves, and each one has its own advantage in certain applications.

Directional control valves can be actuated by several different methods. The following are some examples (also see Fig. 12–11): manual, push-pull lever, pedal, push button, mechanical (cam), electric solenoid, and pilot pressure.

There are several varieties of directional control valves for pneumatic systems. Some of the most popular are:

- the two-way valve—an on or off valve;
- the three-way—has three flow paths and ports pressure to one end and relieves the same end;
- the four-way valve—allows four flow paths through the valve;

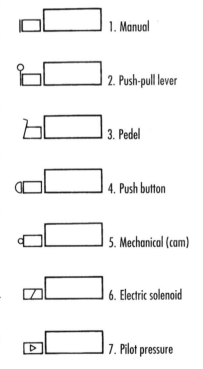

1. Manual

2. Push-pull lever

3. Pedel

4. Push button

5. Mechanical (cam)

6. Electric solenoid

7. Pilot pressure

Figure 12-11.
Directional control valve actuators.

- the 5-port valve—comes in three popular types, center exhaust, all ports blocked center, and both cylinder ports open to pressure center (Fig. 12–12).

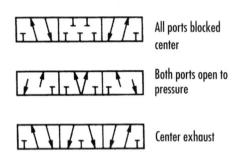

All ports blocked center

Both ports open to pressure

Center exhaust

Figure 12-12. Three common center positions of the 5-port valve.

Each type has its own advantages and disadvantages for use in a pneumatic system. The *center exhaust* allows the actuator to be moved with the valve centered. *All ports blocked center* will not let the actuator move when in the center position (except for the compressibility of the air). The *both ports open to pressure center* holds the actuator in a more rigid position; however, a cylinder has a tendency to move or creep toward the rod end of the cylinder because of the difference in the areas the pressure is applied.

When looking at directional control valves, the number of positions the valve can be found in is determined on the print by the number of envelopes found in the valve diagrams.

Flow Control Valve. The flow control valve (Fig. 12-13) is found next in the circuit. It is used to control the flow into an actuator. This then controls the speed at which the actuator works. There are two basic types of flow controls: the adjustable and the adjustable with bypass. The speed of the actuator can be controlled by allowing more or less flow to the actuator. The bypass allows free flow in one direction, making speed control in one direction possible. If the flow is controlled going into the cylinder, it is a meter-in circuit. If it is controlled coming out of the actuator, then it is a meter-out circuit.

Actuator. The actuator is the last component in the system. There are two types of actuators—cylinders or motors (Fig. 12–14).

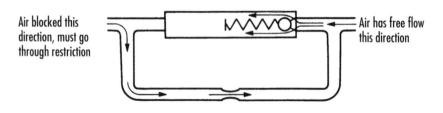

Air blocked this direction, must go through restriction

Air has free flow this direction

Figure 12-13. Flow control valve.

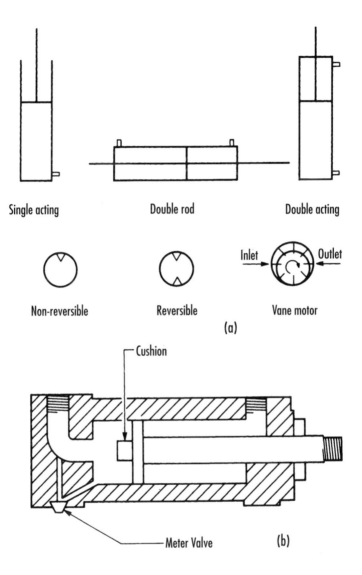

Figure 12-14.   (a) Actuators; (b) air cylinder with cushion.

Cylinder actuators provide linear thrust and straight line motion. There are several types of cylinders. The single acting cylinders apply force in one direction and are spring, weight, or gravity return. The double acting cylinders apply force in both directions, which means it can be driven in both ways. The double rod cylinder applies an equal force in both directions. There are also cushioned cylinders, which slow down at the end of their stroke to prevent shock to the system. The cylinder retracts until the cushion comes in contact with the opening in the end on the cylinder. The air is no longer able to exhaust out of the cylinder unrestricted. The flow is controlled by a small valve. This meters out the air to provide the cushion to slow it down. There are two types: either adjustable or nonadjustable.

Air motor actuators are usually piston or vane motors. They work in just the opposite way of the compressors; the pressurized flow comes in, activates the motor, then is exhausted out. They come in two styles—reversible or nonreversible.

Muffler. One last device that may be found at the actuator or at a directional control valve is the muffler (Fig. 12–15). It reduces the amount of noise created when the air is exhausted to the atmosphere. It has some restriction to flow, so in use there will be some backpressure. Whether this is objectionable to the system is an important consideration before using a muffler.

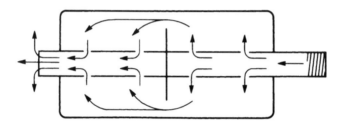

Figure 12-15. Cutaway of a muffler.

Summary

Pneumatic systems will never replace hydraulic systems in industry. However, they have their own place. The speed and low power they offer make them indispensable. If they are properly maintained, they will give many years of dependable service.

Section 2:
Application of the
Zero Breakdown Strategies

The Five Step Process to Implementing Zero Breakdown Strategies

The material covered in the first section of the book dealt with enablers that allow the five steps to zero breakdowns to be successful. It should be noted that unless the previous material has been considered and the enablers adopted (or contingencies developed), the five step process will be suboptimized.

The five-step process is an evolutionary journey. It starts with ensuring that the basics are in place. While this seems repetitive, it cannot be overemphasized that 50% of all equipment breakdowns are related to a lack of understanding how components are designed to function and how to properly maintain the components. If the basics are neglected or treated superficially, then minimal results can be expected when the other Zero Breakdown Strategies are attempted.

The next two steps are to ensure the equipment-related roles and responsibilities are clearly understood by operations and maintenance. Many equipment failures are caused by the facilities or operations departments not having a clear understanding of the equipment or asset's design capabilities and functions. Additional failures are also caused by the maintenance and engineering departments failing to understand and then execute proper maintenance procedures on the equipment or assets.

In addition to possible misunderstanding of the roles and responsibilities of operations and maintenance toward the equipment, there is also the possibility that either of the two groups could make mistakes. So, mistake-proofing the equipment from operational and maintenance perspectives bears close consideration.

Eliminating design problems will prevent some equipment failures and extend the overall equipment life. Unfortunately, this is one of the easiest areas to place blame. When operations or maintenance fail to execute their responsibilities toward the equipment or asset, instead of correcting the situation, they blame it on the design. In reality, very few breakdowns are related to design problems. However, if the previous steps have not solved the equipment or asset problems, then the design should be examined for possible flaws.

When these five areas are closely considered, the pathway to Zero Breakdowns becomes clearer, and sometimes even obvious.

Chapter 13:
Maintaining Basic Conditions

There are three major activities involved in maintaining basic conditions. These are: equipment cleaning, tightening, and lubrication.

Equipment Cleaning

In many companies today these are primarily motivational activities. And while motivation is a good reason to clean equipment, there are also technical reasons to clean equipment. For example, consider an electrical motor. If an electrical motor is allowed to become contaminated, the contamination acts as an insulator, interfering with the thermal transfer process or heat dissipation. This results in a temperature rise of the motor. As the temperature increases, the design life of the motor decreases. One study showed that in some motors the useful life was reduced by $1/2$ for every 10°C rise in operating temperature above the designed operating temperature. This can be a self-destructive problem also, since in some annealed copper wire, a 50°C temperature rise causes a 20% increase in resistance in the wiring. This leads to even more heat, more resistance, and more heat—until the motor fails.

Even if this does not result in an immediate failure of the motor, it may result in getting 6 months of life out of a motor, when it was designed to provide 6 to 10 years of life. This means that unnecessary maintenance will be performed.

Also, consider that gear cases have a similar problem. If gear case exteriors are allowed to become contaminated, the internal temperature of the gear case will rise. As the temperature rises, the manufacturer's suggested lubricant for the gear case is incorrect. The higher temperatures will result in thinning viscosity of the lubricant, creating metal-to-metal contact between components in the gear case. This will result in rapid wear, thus shortening the life of the gear case.

Additionally, consider that standard greases have a ceiling of approximately 175°F before rapid deterioration begins. Beyond that temperature, the lubricant life is reduced, resulting in excessive lubricant changes or wear of the gear case components.

Further temperature rises also create seal and bearing problems. The next level of temperature problem occurs at approximately 225°F, since this is the maximum temperature at which standard seals can be used without rapid wear and failure. Normal bearing steel has a ceiling limit of 250°F as an operating temperature. Beyond that temperature, rapid failure of the bearing results.

As with the motor, the gear case and components will not fail immediately. However, it may need to be replaced after 2 or 3 months of use, rather than 7 or 8 years of use. This leads to excessive maintenance cost and unavailability of the equipment.

Hydraulic systems also have a problem with cleanliness and heat . A hydraulic system is equipped with a reservoir that is designed to dissipate the heat in the hydraulic fluid as it returns to the tank. This cooling function may be enhanced by coolers to lower the temperature of the fluid. If the tank becomes dirty or the coolers become clogged, the temperature of fluid begins to rise. Once it reaches about 140°F, then the hydraulic fluid begins its rapid degradation. One study shows that the hydraulic fluid will oxidize twice as fast for every 20°F temperature rise above 130°. At 215°F, the oil life expectancy will drop to 3% of the original design.

As the oil reaches the end of its life, it loses its lubricating quality, allowing rapid wear of system components, such as pumps, valves, and actuators. This rapid wear produces wear particles and contaminants that will further damage the hydraulic system and degrade its performance.

Another problem related to overheated hydraulic fluids is inlet air leaks or cavitation. As the air bubbles collapse on the pressure side of the pump, the implosions can produce temperatures of up to 2100°F.

Regardless of how the oil is overheated, it will take on a varnished and sticky quality. The varnish particles travel downstream through the pump and other components such as control valves and actuators clogging lines and causing sticking valves that burn out other components. This results in the system failure and downtime, or erratic operation and the related minor stoppages.

Tightening or Torquing Procedures

When discussing proper torquing procedures, one must first consider the proper tools. In many organizations, technicians are observed using crescent wrenches, channel locks, or other tools to tighten hex fasteners. The proper tool, of course, is a torque wrench. A torque wrench can measure the proper amount of torque applied to a faster. This is important, since all threaded fasteners are derived from a simple machine called the incline plane. Mating screw threads are two incline planes wedging against each other. When a fastener has the proper amount of torque applied, it is distorted, locking the threads so they will not loosen.

If a fastener is not torqued sufficiently, it is not deformed, so it will fail to lock, and eventually work loose creating a vibration, wear, and ultimate failure. Conversely, if a fastener is overtightened, it can exceed the elasticity of the fastener material, deforming the fastener so that is weakened. Then the fastener, when retightened, will loosen quickly or break.

Also, it is not enough just to understand the amount of torque to apply to a size of fastener; the amount of torque is also determined by the grade of the fastener. There are many grades of fasteners available and, even in the same size, each requires a different amount of torque. So proper fastening begins with the right tools, and ends with the correct reference material.

Consider how many failures at a plant or a facility occur simply because a mechanical device was not fastened correctly. The fastener would begin to work loose, creating vibration, creating wear, which increases the vibration, which increases the wear, until a failure occurs. This scenario is all too common in plants today. What percent of all failures at a specific plant or facility could be eliminated by paying attention to proper fastening procedures? One study in the petrochemical industry showed that 50% of all fastener failures occur due to improper assembly and incorrect torque.

Even simple practices like never using a nut on a fastener more than twice can cause problems. Bolts and nuts should be match weighted, to ensure a proper fit. While these are basics, they are neglected in many companies today.

Fastening even has applications in bolted couplings. For example, when installing coupling bolts, which is tightened—the bolt or the nut? If the bolt is turned, material is worn from it and the coupling. This results in excess clearances, which creates even greater wear, until both the coupling and the bolts must be changed.

Another area for examination would be the application of bolts in piping flanges. The five most common causes of flange leaks are:

1. Uneven bolt torque.
2. Poor flange alignment.
3. Poor gasket installation.
4. Poor condition of flange faces.
5. Excessive piping strain.

As noted, the first two causes will be related to proper use of the fasteners. A case could be made that all five causes could be impacted by good fastener practices.

Proper Lubrication

As mentioned in Chapter 2, lubricants have two main functions:

1. Minimize friction and wear.
2. Carry off heat generated by the components being lubricated.

Proper lubrication would then include the following items:

- the right lubricant,
- the right quantity of lubricant,
- the right application method, and
- the right frequency of application.

The question might be asked: how often do technicians perform all four of the requirements correctly? Anyone can watch as power grease guns are applied to bearings, the trigger pulled, and the bearing filled until grease oozes out of the seals. However, is that the correct level of lubricant for a pillow block bearing? A pillow block bearing is designed to be filled only one-third full of oil or grease to allow for heat dissipation during operation. So bearings could be overlubricated; they could overheat, and their life would be shortened dramatically.

Sometimes, maintenance is simple, such as minor repairs around lubrication on equipment. For example, a breather on a gear case can become clogged . In some cases, the breather may be missing and a replacement required. In many cases, the replacement for a plugged up or missing breather is a pipe plug. The pipe plug does not allow for air expansion when the gear case becomes warm. As air pressure increases in the gear case, the lubricant is forced out of the seal. This creates leaks and collects contamination. As the gear case cools, the air is drawn in, pulling contamination against and through the seal. This increases the wear rate of the seal and leads to premature failure of the seal as well as contamination of the lubricant.

Lubrication also needs to be monitored for contamination. Any contaminants in the lubricant will eventually come between the components in a drive and accelerate the wear on the component. There are three main sources of contamination.

1. Built in contamination—which includes residual sand, metal chips, weld spatter, thread sealant, etc.

2. Generated contamination—wear particles, seal fragments, degraded lubricants, etc.
3. Introduced contamination—airborne dirt, absorbents, and water.

All of these forms of contaminants can increase the wear on the components.

Water is also a contaminant, but it acts differently. Water has no load-carrying capability. As water moves between the moving components at a drive, the fluid film barrier is ruptured and metal-to-metal contact occurs. This accelerates wear in the gear case or drive. For example, water content does the following:

- 0.03% water content reduces bearing life to 50% of L-10 rating
- 0.2% water content reduces bearing life to 17% of L-10 rating
- 1% water content reduces bearing life to 6.3% of L-10 rating
- 2% water content reduces bearing life to 4% of L-10 rating.

With mineral oil, 20 ppm water content reduces roller bearing life by 48%. By these figures, it is quite easy to see the dramatic impact that even the slightest water content has on the life of the lubricated components.

Water can enter lubricants even in storage. If barrels of lubricant products are stored outdoors in a vertical position, water can accumulate on top of the drum. Normal heating and cooling during the day will create expansion and contraction of the air pocket in the drum. This will actually pull drops of water down the screw threads of the bung and into the lubricant. When the lubricant is used, water is introduced into the drive, shortening the life of the components.

Mixing lubricants can also create problems. Since different vendors use different additives to their lubricants, mixing incompatible lubricants will cause a chemical reaction. This leads to the formation of acids and alkaloids, or can thin viscosity, thicken viscosity, cause coagulation, etc. It is important to always understand the interchange requirements and consequences of using certain lubricants before mixing them.

Chapter 14:
Maintaining Operating Standards

Maintaining operating standards requires setting the design capacity for a particular piece of equipment. The goal is then to achieve this design capacity, not to exceed it. Unfortunately, many companies today believe that exceeding design capacity is good. However, as design capacity is exceeded, service life and reliability of the equipment is reduced. While the speed or the instant output of the equipment may look good, the resulting downtime negatively impacts the overall capacity.

Many companies struggle to understand or find design capacity for their equipment. However, there are many methods available. The first is to consult the manufacturer. The manufacturer should be able to provide design capacity documentation for the equipment. Another option is to find a similar-use customer who knows the design capacity of the equipment. A third option is to consult the history records of the equipment to see what had been achieved in the past and to establish the reliability of the equipment. Using these methods, a company should be able to determine the design capacity of the equipment.

Standardizing Operating Methods

In many organizations, maintenance employees can look at the production scheduling board and determine by the operator schedule what equipment will break down. Quite simply, this is because different operators will operate the equipment using various procedures. Operator variability has a definite impact on equipment reliability. The solution to this problem is proper training of the operators and the development of standardized operating procedures. If the operators are trained and the procedures are followed, then it will not be difficult to have standardized operating methods.

Operating Conditions

When equipment is installed and operated, it must be operated in the environmental conditions in which the equipment was designed to function. There should not be excessive temperature (either too hot or too cold), excessive vibration, or shock loads. The equipment should be operated as it was designed to be operated. Any variance outside operating parameters specified by the vendor will contribute to unreliable equipment.

This also applies to the storage conditions for major spares or components for this equipment. Major spares should be stored in suitable conditions to prolong the life of the spare part. If subassemblies and spares are not stored correctly, when they are installed on the equipment they will provide less than satisfactory service, both from a reliability and a life-cycle perspective.

Construction Standards

When equipment is installed, the construction standards must be as specified by the manufacturer of the equipment. This means that during the installation, there should be a proper foundation so that there is no undue stress placed on the component. Assemblies requiring attachment to supporting structures, such as a piping, should also be installed with no strain from the supporting or attached structures. Piping strain can quickly contribute to misalignment of couplings and excessive wear on the related equipment components, such as bearings.

A brief consideration of the foundation for equipment during an installation can help highlight the problem. The foundation is designed to support the static forces of weight and stress. It must also dampen the dynamic forces of vibration and any shock loads.

When a foundation cracks, it allows contaminants to penetrate the foundation and degrade the concrete. This requires a repair to be made to the foundation. This is usually some form of grout replacement. Attention must be given to the storage of the grout. Grout stored outside during the summer will have a hot cure. This means that the grout will cure in a thermally expanded state. When the grout cools, there are stresses that are locked in the grout. Eventually these stresses will be relieved, and excessive cracking will result.

For a foundation to provide satisfactory service, the following points need to be considered:

- proper chemistry,
- proper water and cement ratios,
- quality of the aggregate,
- a low amount of entrained air,
- placement must be proper for load,
- proper temperature range for curing,
- proper humidity maintained during curing, and
- Proper time for curing—7 uninterrupted days for most foundations.

Now, if this level of detail is required just for the foundation, what about the level of detail for the rest of the installation steps? Do most companies pay attention to the detail, or do they just hook it up and get it running? It is little wonder that the equipment in many plants fails to perform to design specifications.

Electrical supplies and other utilities also need to be carefully examined when the equipment is installed. These areas tend to be a problem when equipment is moved temporarily or is moved frequently, as in some manufacturing operations. Any time equipment is moved and is expected to be utilized in operations, it must be installed correctly to obtain design capacity and reliability.

Elimination of Contamination

As part of maintaining operating standards, equipment should be kept clean. However, this in itself is not sufficient. Once equipment is cleaned, the sources of contamination, moisture, process wastes, etc., must be eliminated. Unless this is accomplished, the equipment will not remain clean, and ultimately the contamination will impact the reliability of the equipment.

Chapter 15:
Deterioration Prevention

Deterioration prevention focuses on the maintenance of equipment, whereas operating standards focus more on the operation of equipment. Deterioration prevention covers things such as establishing equipment baselines, standardizing repair policies and procedures, and standardizing of spare parts.

Equipment Restoration

Equipment restoration implies that equipment is to be maintained at a certain baseline level. The equipment does not have to be restored to an as-new condition, but the baseline must be acceptable for achieving design capacity, quality, and reliability. If the equipment is worn out, then predictive techniques such as vibration analysis cannot be used effectively. Vibration analysis would try to read all sources of vibration, and if the equipment is worn out or in a substandard condition, there would be too many transient vibration signals for vibration analysis to be effective. The same would hold true for other predictive techniques if the equipment is not kept at a baseline. Once the equipment is at the baseline, then predictive monitoring techniques can be effective in finding and trending deterioration. With this information, action can be taken to correct certain conditions, and to keep the equipment at an acceptable baseline.

Predictive and Reliability Tools

Once the equipment is at an acceptable baseline, then MTBF (Mean Time Between Failure) and MTTR (Mean Time To Repair) calculations can be used to track the equipment condition to ensure that excessive breakdowns or long breakdowns are not occurring. In addition, technologies such as vibration analysis, oil analysis, thermography, and sonics can be used to spot wear or deterioration, and to alert the maintenance workforce that a restoration process is required for the equipment.

Standardization of Repair Policies and Procedures

As discussed earlier, operator variability will impact the reliability of the equipment; similarly, maintenance variability will impact equipment reliability. Just as the operators may operate the equipment differently, two maintenance technicians may perform the same repair differently, with different results, and with (perhaps) different mistakes. In fact, the same analogy applies: there are occasions when the operators will look at the maintenance schedule to see which maintenance technicians are working. If certain ones are working, the operators may wait to ask for a job to be done, since they are concerned the maintenance technicians working do not have the skills to do the job right. The solution to this problem is similar to the operations situation: proper training and development of standardized job plans for each of the major maintenance tasks. This will ensure that the equipment is rebuilt or repaired exactly the same way, and the proper reliability and utilization of the equipment can be achieved.

Standardized Spare Parts

It is important that the inventory and purchasing people purchase equivalent OEM spare parts. In many cases, when maintenance specifies a spare part, the purchasing department, in an attempt to save money, will buy a spare part that is not exactly as specified. This creates problems with equipment reliability and may actually increase downtime. It is not cost-effective if the component must be changed two or three times just to save a few dollars on the price of the spare. The downtime and lost capacity will negate any small savings purchasing made on the cost of spare parts.

So spare parts must be of a quality equivalent to the OEM. Another issue regarding spare parts is purchasing them when needed—that is, not over purchasing —because spare parts actually deteriorate while on the shelf. Some companies will purchase MRO components in bulk and, in some cases, the shelf life expires before the stock can be used. In an attempt to prevent this, many companies develop good supplier relationships so that the parts can be delivered "just in time."

Storage of Spare Parts

In many instances, spare parts are stored incorrectly in maintenance storage areas. For example, many bearings are unwrapped and left open on the shelf in storage. Unwrapping a bearing actually begins its deterioration. Bearings are extremely sensitive components and need to be protected while in storage.

Simply unwrapping a bearing and handling it with bare hands can start deterioration. The pH balance in the human body is so acidic that it will actually began to corrode a bearing if the steel is touched with dry hands. This corrosion leads to pitting, and interferes with proper shaft and housing fits and, in some cases, can actually deteriorate the raceway of the bearing.

Also, V-belts are components that can deteriorate quickly. In many companies, V-belts tend to be stored at high elevations on pegs in the storage areas. While this in itself is not incorrect, if the temperature toward the higher level in the stores area is 120°F or above during the summer, this reinitializes the vulcanization process that was used to create the belts in the first place. This temperature will overcure the compound of the V-belts, rendering them white and brittle. The belts must be stored at room temperature if they are to be protected in storage.

In some plants, major components of rotating equipment are sitting motionless in storage. While this may not seem bad itself, two out of three ingredients in the recipe for deterioration of the equipment are present: a bearing not rotating, and mounted under load. The third ingredient that is needed to complete the destruction of the component is some form of external vibration. If there is a punch press, overhead crane, forklift, or even sonic vibration, this will cause vibration in the bearing. This creates a microscopic rocking action in the bearing that eventually will rupture the stationary fluid film barrier. This results in metal-to-metal contact that destroys the bearing. This is a condition known as a false brinelling and is widely known in the bearing industry. Unfortunately, many companies do not understand this problem, so some components are allowed to deteriorate. Then, when installed, they last a very short time before failing. The individual rebuilding the component is usually blamed, when actually the component was destroyed in storage.

Some companies also have "bone yards" where they store major spare parts and assemblies outside in the elements. When the component is needed, they will go outside and dig it out of the field and install it; then they wonder why it fails after a short time. If components are stored outdoors, they must be protected from condensation and moisture, heat, cold, etc. Some companies will lose hundreds of thousands of dollars annually in component cost and unnecessary equipment downtime due to major spare parts deteriorating as they sit out in the open.

Accessibility of Equipment

In some cases, it may take longer to assemble a piece of equipment in order to get at a worn component than it does to change the component itself. This has an impact on the mean time to repair calculation (MTTR), or, simply put, the time it takes to repair a component when it fails. Equipment should be designed or redesigned so that it is accessible for inspections, services, and minor adjustments. If this is not done, it will result in unnecessary downtime, with the resulting lost capacity, as well as substandard performance.

Chapter 16:
Improving Design Weaknesses

Design weaknesses in the equipment can be eliminated by strengthening the various parts to extend component life. This may mean improving wear resistance: the material in a high wear area is changed to a material that has a higher wear rating than the components around it.

In a similar way, corrosion resistance may be improved by changing the material to one that is more corrosion-resistant than the material around it in order to improve the process reliability. There may be occasions where stress in the design of the components is the issue, and the design must be changed to minimize the existing stress and fatigue.

It may be necessary to change materials and shapes of items so that they increase their reliability. There may also be the need to improve assembly accuracy so equipment is assembled correctly. While all of these are great ideas to correct design weaknesses, there is one major problem with assuming a design weakness. How many people really know the design life of basic components? The first part of this book dealt almost exclusively on the basics. Now the importance of the basics is reinforced here.

For example, what is the design life of a V-belt? In some companies, V-belts are changed every three to six months. This is a waste of manpower, spare parts, and equipment capacity. The true design life of a properly rated, properly installed, and properly maintained V-belt is three years of continuous operation, or 24,000 hours. Yet, many companies change V-belts much more frequently.

However, this is not a design problem, it is usually an installation and maintenance problem. For example, how many companies really follow the proper procedure outlined previously in this book when installing a V-belt? Installers may pry the belts on, run belts on, or jog units to get belts on—but they do not follow proper procedures. They seldom check alignment, they seldom check tension properly, or they seldom check for sheave wear. All of these bad habits can cause a great reduction in the life of a V-belt.

Another example is the installation and maintenance of roller chain. The design life of roller chain properly installed, properly rated, and properly maintained is seven years. Roller chain installed improperly and improperly lubricated has an expected life of nine days. This is a tremendous difference in life expectancies. It is not a design problem, but more likely it is going to be a maintenance and installation problem. For example, some companies will continue to install a new roller chain over worn-out sprockets. A chain and sprocket should be changed at the same time (a maximum of three replacement chains can be achieved). While this may seem excessive, it is the recommendation.

However, some companies may find that they can allow one sprocket to wear out four or five chains before changing the sprocket. In reality, it must be kept in mind that when the chain is worn out, a similar amount of hardened material is worn from the sprocket. The tooth geometries change as the chain wears against them. Once the chain is worn, the tooth geometries are changed enough so that it will increase the wear on the second chain; a corresponding increase will occur for the third chain, and the fourth chain, accelerating the wear until the chain fails very shortly after installation. It is only by understanding proper installation and maintenance practices of these components that design weaknesses can ever truly be identified.

Bearings are yet another example. How many bearings in a typical plant actually achieve the L-10 rating of the bearing? In most cases, the bearings never achieve the design life, simply because they are mishandled, installed incorrectly, or maintained incorrectly. One study showed that less than 5% of pump bearings in the petrochemical industry ever reach the L-10 rating. The actual rating is over 15 years, yet the majority of the bearings (95%) average just over 1 year of actual usage. Some companies changed bearings on a weekly or monthly basis when, in reality, they should be achieving years of use from the bearing. Another study showed that just about two-thirds of bearing failures are caused by user-induced problems. These problems include maintenance issues, operational issues, and construction/installation issues.

A fourth example is gears. When installed and maintained correctly, gears will show gradual wear patterns. Gears are designed so that there will be no sudden failure of the gear. If there is a sudden failure, then it will either be a maintenance problem or some problem with the operation or shock loads. Gear wear should be able to be plotted and trended over time, and predictable normal wear failures will occur. With gears, another study showed that two-thirds of gear failures were related to controllable causes. These causes include maintenance issues, handling issues, contamination issues, etc.

Best Practices?

What do some workers do—or fail to do—that shortens the design life of equipment and components? Do you see plant technicians installing bearings with hammers? What impact does this have on the design life of the bearing? Have technicians ever been observed welding on the same plane with bearings, allowing the electric arc to pass through the bearing? This, again, dramatically shortens the life of the bearing.

In the case of roller chain, if repair sections are placed in the chain, or special links are inserted, this introduces different forces in the chain drive that will accelerate the wear. The chain will experience tight loads and light loads as the worn and new chain simultaneously operate. This creates tremendous wear on all affected components.

Consider coupling alignment. What techniques are used to align couplings? Is it a tapered gauge? A feeler gauge? A dial indicator? A reverse dial indicator? Is it laser alignment? The point here is that accurate alignment is critical. Any alignment that is made with over three-thousandths (0.003") tolerance will contribute to rapid wear of—and impact the life of—the drive components. Yet many companies will consider the alignment correct as long as the coupling bolts can be put in the coupling. What does this do to the design life of the components?

Studies show that couplings have a higher user-induced failure rate than most components. Approximately 75% of coupling failures are related to maintenance, installation, and contamination issues. Consider some facts about couplings.

1. The reverse dial indicator method is considered the minimum method used to align couplings operating at 3600 RPM or greater (laser is preferred).
2. Coupling and shaft require less than a 0.0005 *loose fit* for speeds under 3600 RPM.
3. Coupling and shafts require a 0.0003 to 0.0005 *interference fit* for speeds above 3600 RPM.
4. The coupling hub requires at least an 85% contact with the shaft to prevent overstressing of the hub and premature failure of the coupling.

Even temperature differentials in alignment can be critical. For example, aligning a new component when it's cold, and then increasing its temperature, will affect the alignment. Thermal expansion on a 20-foot drive train can be as much as 0.20" when going from a cold install state to a warm operating state.

Vibration

Any source of internal or external vibration can be a contributing factor to premature equipment or component failure. Vibration can be a contributing factor to excessive wear in bearings, shafts, belts, chains, gears, pumps, motors, or virtually any other component, dramatically reducing their service life. Vibration can be transmitted by structural support and can actually impact components at a considerable distance from the source. In addition, the structural component transmitting the vibration can be stressed.

Generated vibration also decreases equipment performance, since the vibration requires energy to be created and requires energy to be transmitted. This drain on the energy source for the component causes sub-standard performance, impacting the operation.

Vibration in industrial equipment is detrimental and its impact on equipment effectiveness is overlooked in most plants and facilities.

Summary

All of these issues must be considered before assuming a particular problem is a design fault. In many cases, companies will blame chronic equipment problems on the design engineer or the equipment manufacturer. Upon closer examination, it is found that, in most cases, the root cause of the problem is a maintenance or operational issue. These issues should be addressed first, so that the true design flaw will be clearly identified. Then the design problems can be dealt with properly.

It is beyond the scope of this text to deal with actual design weaknesses related to equipment. It is acknowledged that they do exist and need to be corrected. There are volumes of reference works that deal with the topic of design flaws and enhancements that are available. Most technical libraries carry these texts.

However, as a final note, do not assume that chronic equipment problems are always design issues. Most equipment problems are related to a basic root cause already mentioned in this text. If these issues are examined first, the solutions can be quickly implemented. This process will then make resources available to concentrate on solving real design problems.

Chapter 17:
Preventing Human Error

Human error will exist in at least two areas of a plant. The first to be considered is operations. If a piece of equipment it is observed to be misoperated, what really is the cause of the misoperation?

- Is it possible that the operator was never correctly trained to operate the equipment?
- Is it possible that the equipment was not designed for operability?

When these are considered, do we investigate the possibility of providing some form of interlock to prevent misoperation?

The real cure is to develop standardized operating procedures, and ensure that all operators are identically trained to operate the equipment.

ISO-9000 standards require that the operators are to be trained to such a level that when they rotate from equipment to equipment, there is not the slightest variation in the quality of the product produced. If this was really accomplished in companies today, two things would occur. First, the operators would be so skilled that product quality would never be an issue (an ISO-9000 objective). Second, any equipment deterioration would be quickly identified and corrected before it reached the level where it would impact product quality (another ISO-9000 objective).

Unfortunately, there are very few structured operator training programs in industry today. Most are word of mouth on-the-job training, or learn-as-you-do programs. Structured operator training programs with testing for skills proficiency would eliminate most of the operator errors in industry today.

What if the human error lies in the maintenance department? Then again, ask what caused the mistake? Is it possible that there are:

- poor working conditions
- poor tools and equipment
- poor support structures
- poor troubleshooting information and procedures?

So when examining maintenance errors, consider the working conditions. It is usually hot, dirty, and dark when maintenance makes most repairs. Is it easy to make a mistake in these conditions? The answer, of course, is "yes." So can the conditions be improved to make it easier to make repairs without making mistakes? The answer again is "yes!"

Improving tools and equipment is also important. There are new technologies, new tools and new equipment that can help maintenance workers make repairs more accurately and quickly than in the past. Are the maintenance departments using those tools at all plants and facilities? Definitely not! In many plants and facilities, the attitude is negative about the maintenance function. Subsequently, they never get the tools and equipment necessary to achieve "World Class" levels of performance.

Consider also—from a design perspective—are proper support structures such as auxiliary hoists and booms put in place when the equipment is installed? If so, this will make repairs much easier and quicker. In many plants and facilities, something must be rigged up each time the repairs to be made. This impacts the amount of time it takes to do the repair and increases the related downtime.

Consider the age of the workforce. If the experienced individuals in the workforce leave their jobs, how would the current workforce cope with that loss? Is it possible to develop troubleshooting flowcharts and guides to help assist inexperienced individuals in troubleshooting, thus shortening repair times?

Artificial intelligence systems are currently being developed for maintenance. This may be the way of the future to help eliminate unnecessary equipment downtime.

Chapter 18:
Beyond The Basics

Elimination of Minor Problems

In most companies, the majority of resources are expended trying to solve chronic or large breakdowns. Once the Zero Breakdown Strategies have been effectively implemented, there will be resources and time available to examine minor problems. Minor problems pose a challenge to most technicians, since the causes of minor problems are not obvious. In some cases, the minor problems are not repeatable on demand. This makes troubleshooting more difficult. It may require the technician to be at the equipment for hours to observe the problem. In organizations still wrestling with larger problems, this would seem to be a waste of resources, or nonproductive. This highlights the change of paradigms for an organization when dealing with what is considered to be "productive maintenance work."

This paradigm starts with the attitude toward maintenance technicians in the current organization. Are "heroes" valued? Heroes are those who can go out and take a seemingly major equipment problem and reduce it to a level that allows production to continue for a time period—to the end of the shift or end of the week. These types of individuals are typically valued highly in a reactive maintenance organization.

In an organization that is well along in its trip to Zero Breakdowns, this individual begins to lose importance. The individual that becomes more valued is one who can perform a root cause analysis—an individual who can permanently solve problems. This type of individual may not seem as dynamic as a hero, but their effect on the equipment or asset will be considerable. If an organization has the attitude that an individual does not work fast enough, or they always take longer than someone else to do a job, then this type of individual is probably not valued.

The organization must change its paradigm, otherwise the technicians required for a company to be competitive in the future will be working for the competition.

Considerations for Improvement

The following are items that should be considered when trying to eliminate minor problems.

Monitor Slight Defects. Monitoring slight defects requires the development of manual- or technology-based inspections that find developing wear or defects in the asset/equipment before a problem develops. The manual inspections can be developed using material presented previously in this text, or related material found in other texts, vendor manuals, manufacturer recommendations, etc.

Technology-based inspections would require the utilization of techniques such as vibration analysis, oil analysis, thermography, or other nondestructive techniques. Specifications for developing these inspections can be found in textbooks, manufacturer's recommendations, or technical presentations in magazine articles, or conference presentations by other companies with similar equipment.

The goal is to track and trend equipment/asset wear and then schedule the appropriate maintenance task in a just in time mode to prevent an impact on the asset utilization.

Maintain Equipment/Asset Baselines. When an asset or equipment item is designed, constructed, and installed, there are certain baselines as to performance, operating conditions, and physical conditions specified. Maintaining the baselines ensures that the baseline specifications are monitored and maintained. Since any variance from the baselines will result in a negative impact on the equipment performance, corrections to restore the baseline conditions are planned and scheduled prior to the variance becoming objectionable. While similar to the previous activity, this varies since it also includes the environmental conditions in which the equipment is operating.

Review Operator and Maintenance Technician Skills. This was mentioned at the beginning of the book as an enabler, and was covered as one of the steps to Zero Breakdown Strategies. It is important to consider at this point also since the skills of those involved in operating or maintaining the equipment can have minor impact on the equipment that is cumulative. When considered individually, the problem may only account for a few minutes per shift. However, when this is multiplied times the number of shifts in a week, number of employees involved, number of weeks in a year, and so on, it becomes an extremely large problem.

The emphasis must be placed on small things, since at this stage of the Zero Breakdown process, only little things are left to examine. At this point, what is now accepted as chronic problems, or "that's just the way it is," need to be questioned and closely examined. Many companies have added considerable capacity to their equipment/assets by paying close attention to the skills of their employees. Standard operating procedures will usually play a large role in high-lighting and solving this problem.

Develop Problem Resolution Procedures. The procedures to resolve equipment or asset problems should be part of a disciplined, data-driven process. It should not be the decision of one person to make changes to operating or maintenance directives. This would result in one shift running the equipment one way, and another shift doing it differently. This would result in chaos and make it virtually impossible to do any root causes analysis if a problem did develop.

Simple first. In solving problems, simple issues should be addressed first. Again, if this recommendation is implemented at the proper stage of Zero Breakdowns, all that should be left to address are simple problems.

Also, complex problems tend to be simple problems that have been let go too long, or simple problems that have compounded. Compound simple problems appear to be complex and will still need to be traced back to the root cause, and the solution implemented at that level.

Complex second. Complex problems may occur, but should never have become complex due to a combination of simple problems. Complex problems could be developed through design errors, operational errors, and maintenance errors, combining into a jigsaw puzzle of various root causes.

Solving these types of complex problems may require the use of fishbone diagrams or other problem solving tools. Usually complex problems can be broken into multiple root causes, and the solutions developed at that level.

Act on each occurrence. The simple message here is do not procrastinate. When problems develop, solve them when they are small. Problems only grow in one direction. They only get larger and more complex. Solving them while they are small can save a company a lot of time and capacity. The financial impact of lost efficiency and capacity will be addressed in the next section.

Financial Measurements and the Overall Equipment Effectiveness

Unless there is a clear financial benefit to the Zero Breakdown Strategy initiative, management's attention will be diverted in the near future to another acronym of the month. There will be another "World Class" program that promises to make the company more competitive and increase the profits. Zero Breakdown Strategies will be another of the "we tried that" initiatives that companies have in their program archives.

However, it doesn't have to be like this. Many equipment-related strategies have been suboptimized in many companies today simply because when they were being implemented no one had the vision to build a business case or a cost benefit analysis. In fact, many companies begin focusing their activities on the wrong equipment in their plants simply because the financial impact was not understood.

Where should the initial efforts in a plant focus? In order to maximize the return on investment that a company makes in Zero Breakdowns, the efforts must focus on the critical equipment in the plant. Critical equipment may also be referred to as constraint equipment. This is equipment that, if it would operate and produce the way it was originally designed, would make a significant difference to the plant operation. For example, it could be an equipment item that is a production bottleneck. It could be an equipment item that requires a high level of maintenance resources to keep it running.

Once the critical equipment is identified, it is important to "benchmark" its performance. This benchmark is called the *Overall Equipment Effectiveness,* or OEE. The OEE is calculated by the following formula:

OEE = Availability × Performance Efficiency × Quality Rate.

Availability is the time the equipment is scheduled to run divided by the time the equipment is available to run, expressed as a percentage. The goal here is at least 90%. (Remember, this is not just for the maintenance downtime, but all downtime.) Some companies don't like to use the total time available to run, since the equipment could be running a 7 × 24 schedule and they are only running the equipment a 5 × 24 schedule. However, this shows that there is excess capacity for the equipment, if they wanted to utilize it. Instead, many companies will purchase another equipment item and thereby increase their cost of the asset base. This negatively impacts corporate financial indicators such as return on net assets. It is best to understand the true availability of the equipment, rather than hiding it by allowing for exceptions to the calculation.

Some companies will choose to use the scheduled run time divided by the actual run time, realizing that the equipment has unused capacity. This allows the personnel to concentrate on maximizing the equipment performance during the scheduled time, always realizing that there is additional capacity if it is ever needed.

Performance Efficiency is the rate the equipment is operating divided by the design rate of operation, expressed as a percentage. The goal here is at least

95%. There are two common mistakes for this calculation. First, some companies will reengineer the equipment or higher performance standards and not reflect this by changing the design rate of operation. This gives them a performance efficiency of over 100%, which is misleading and subsequently could hide other areas of weakness in the OEE.

The second mistake is not really understanding the design specifications of the equipment. This is especially a problem with older equipment. It has been here for so long, that no one remembers what the design performance specifications really were. So the equipment performance is accepted at the level of what someone remembers that it "used to do." This typically is far below the design and, again, the OEE calculation is impacted. The lack of data hides the true potential of the equipment.

The *quality rate* is the product produced minus the off-spec product divided by the product produced. This percentage should be in the 99%+ range. The most common mistake here is defining what constitutes a defect. Clearly, a defect is anything that is not first pass quality. Any rework, refiltering, repackaging, or reformatting is not first pass quality.

A sample might look like this:

> Availability = 85%
> Performance Efficiency = 90%
> Quality Rate = 95%
> OEE = 0.85 × 0.90 × 0.95 or 72.6%

If the goal is 85% (0.90 × 0.95 × 0.99), then 72.6% may not seem so bad. However, this is where an improvement needs to be made in the OEE calculation. If the question of "What impact is this making on our profit picture?" was asked, the answer will not be acceptable. Simply saying that the OEE has gone from 72% to 85% will not satisfy the financial personnel.

The correct answer is derived by "dollarizing" the OEE. This means that the production output for an OEE of 72% must be compared to the production output for an OEE of 85%, in real dollars. Consider this example.

Production output for 72% OEE =	15,600 pieces (any production measure)
Production output for 85% OEE =	<u>23,400 pieces</u>
Difference =	7,800 pieces
Cost per piece	× <u>$12.00</u>
Dollar value per week -	$93,600.00
Annualized (50 week year)	× <u> 50</u>
Total value of increased Throughput	$4,680,000.00

Now, if the scenario is played out the third time and the question "What impact is this making on our profit picture?" is asked, the answer is clear and in terms the financial personnel will understand. In fact, if additional funding was required for additional tools, training, or personnel, the return on the investment would be easy for anyone to calculate.

Zero Breakdown Strategies is more than just another program that companies can implement. It is really an operating philosophy that is tied to the company's profit picture. Unless the efforts are connected to the bottom line, there is little chance of it really succeeding in a company. While certain activities are a part of Zero Breakdown Strategies, unless a financial approach is taken to highlight the benefits, long-term viability of the initiative will be doubtful.

Chapter 19:
Financial Considerations of Zero Breakdown Strategies

Zero Breakdowns: A Cost or Profit?

In an effort to become more competitive, managers are turning over every stone to find areas for improvement and cost savings. As they study the asset management, companies find that maintenance makes up anywhere from 15% to 40% of total product cost. They also discover that dollars saved in maintenance are a cost avoidance. If they take the typical profit margins for manufacturing companies, they discover that one dollar saved in maintenance costs contributes as much to company profits as $20.00 in new sales. In larger companies, reducing maintenance expenditures by $1 million contributes as much to profits as increasing sales by $20 million. In competitive markets, all companies find that being able to improve maintenance and decrease unnecessary maintenance expenditures by $1 million is much easier and more likely to occur than finding $20 million in new sales.

The following pages present guidelines for calculating the savings that a company may achieve by implementing Zero Breakdown Strategies.

The purpose of this material is to present ways of examining the effect of Zero Breakdown Strategies on a company's cost structure. The material is organized to allow various parts to be used where applicable and omitted where not. This approach allows individual companies to customize the benefits to meet their own circumstances.

Standard Cost Justification

This discussion of standard cost justification consists of four main parts:

1. asset (or equipment) maintenance labor costs,
2. asset spare part costs,
3. downtime/availability costs, and
4. project cost savings.

Asset (or Equipment) Maintenance Labor Costs. Maintenance productivity in most American companies averages between 25% and 35%. This translates into less than 3 hours per 8-hour shift of hands-on activities. Most of the lost productivity can be attributed to the following reasons:

- waiting on parts
- waiting on information, drawings, instructions, etc.
- waiting for the equipment to be shut down
- waiting on rental equipment to arrive
- waiting on other crafts to finish their part of the job
- running from emergency to emergency.

While 100% productivity is an unrealistic goal for any maintenance organization, a more realistic percentage of 60% is achievable.

The productivity of maintenance technicians can be improved by concentrating on basic management techniques such as:

- planning jobs in advance,
- scheduling jobs and coordinating schedules with operations,
- arranging for the parts to be ready when needed,
- coordinating the tools, rental equipment, etc., and
- reducing the emergency work below the 50% level by PMs (preventive maintenance tasks).

With computer assistance, planning time per job is reduced, resulting in more jobs planned and coordinated. This results in more time for preventive maintenance activities, which in turn helps to reduce the amount of emergency and breakdown activities. This results in fewer schedule changes and helps to increase the productivity by reducing travel and waiting time. Companies successful in gaining control of the maintenance labor resources have reported increases in productivity of as much as 28%.

Asset Spare Part Costs. Spare part costs are related to the frequency and size of the repairs made to a company's equipment. The sheer number of parts, in addition to the stores policies, purchasing policies, and overall inventory management practices, contribute to the overall cost of asset/equipment maintenance materials. Since little attention is paid to asset/equipment spare parts in some companies, inventories may be higher than necessary by some 20% to 30%. This increases inventory holding costs and makes spare parts unnecessarily expensive. The inability of stores to service the organization's need for spares often results in "pirate" or "illegal" storage depots for just-in-case spares. This practice, too, drives up the cost of asset/equipment spare parts.

Good inventory controls enable companies to lower the value of the inventory and still maintain a service level of 95% to 97%. This efficiency enables the asset/equipment maintenance department to be responsive to the operations group, while increasing its own personal productivity. Successful companies have averaged 19% lower material costs, and an overall 18% reduction in total inventory.

Downtime/Availability Costs. Downtime/availability costs are potentially the source of the greatest savings for a company determined to implement Zero Breakdown Strategies. Downtime cost for equipment may vary from several hundreds of dollars per hour to literally hundreds of thousands of dollars per hour. For example, one company has several production lines in its plant, and downtime on each is worth $1 million per 24 hours of downtime.

In some companies, downtime levels can run as high as 30% or even more. This downtime results in lost sales opportunities, unnecessary expenditures for capital equipment, and generally puts the company in a weak competitive position. By dedicating the company to focusing on Zero Breakdown Strategies and using a CMMS (EAM) as a tracking tool, equipment downtime can be reduced dramatically. Successful companies have averaged a 20% reduction in equipment downtime losses.

Project Cost Savings. As a subset of equipment downtime, project, outage, or refurbishing activities should also be considered. These activities, if not properly controlled, can have a dramatic impact on a company's production capacity. The reason for this impact is that these activities are usually performed with the asset/equipment in a down condition. This means there is no production from the equipment during this time. For that reason, any time eliminated from a project, an outage, or a refurbishing activity can be converted to production time.

Improved planning and coordination can be achieved with a Zero Breakdown Strategy Initiative, since equipment conditions are accurately known. In addition, increased planning and control of information about the assets/equipment will reduce unnecessary downtime during the project. Successful companies have indicated an average of 5% reduction in outage time.

Additional Savings Considerations

Warranty Costs for Equipment. In companies that have recently purchased equipment, this is an area of possible savings. In many instances, some of the repairs made on equipment under warranty are reimbursable under a purchase and service agreement with the equipment supplier. The amount of the reimbursement can vary, but companies have found that 5% to 10% of all work performed on equipment covered by warranties may be reimbursed.

There are some questions you might want to consider when investigating warranty savings. The questions pinpoint areas that may make the compliance with warranty provisions difficult. They are:

- In order to be covered by the warranty, do the repairs have to be made by or supervised by a representative of the supplier company?
- If the repairs are made by internal technicians, does it void the warranty?
- What level of documentation must be provided to the supplier to collect under the terms of the warranty?

If the concerns addressed in these questions would impact the warranty, your company may want to consider whether it is worth the effort. For example, what if a critical piece of equipment would have to remain shut down while you wait for the supplier's representative to arrive and make or oversee the repairs? The cost of the downtime would no doubt quickly exceed the monies that could be regained from warranty claims.

There are opportunities to receive reimbursements for repairs made to equipment under warranty. However, a company would want to make a serious cost/benefit evaluation before these are actively pursued.

Energy Cost Savings. It should be noted that the increased attention given to the assets/equipment under a Zero Breakdown Strategies Initiative will contribute to these savings. However, the major savings will be derived from ensuring that a comprehensive and effective preventive maintenance program is utilized.

In order to effectively calculate energy cost savings, it is necessary for a company to know its energy usage. If this is not known, industry averages can be used for a quick estimate of the savings. Studies by engineering institutes and international companies show that a company can cut energy consumption at a plant by 5% to 11%, depending upon their current preventive maintenance effort. Companies with good preventive maintenance programs can still realize savings in the 5% range, when combining these efforts with Zero Breakdown Strategies. Companies with little or no preventive maintenance inspections and services can realize savings in the 10% range. Following are some examples of energy savings for typical systems.

1. *Mechanical Systems*. Energy savings in mechanical systems result from good preventive maintenance performed on basic mechanical components. For example, how accurate are couplings aligned in your mechanical sys-

tems? Misalignment by even 0.003 inches can lead to energy loss through the coupling. This loss is typically displayed as heat energy in the flex member of the coupling and the supporting shaft bearings. Even elastomer couplings will display energy loss.

A second type of mechanical loss is V-belt slippage. Improper tension can result in slippage during loading on the belt. This loss is again shown as heat in the contact area between the belt and the sheave. Chain and gear misalignment will also waste energy in the transmission area and in bearings. Poor maintenance practices and inadequate preventive maintenance can contribute to a 5% to 10% energy loss for mechanical power transmission systems.

2. *Electrical Systems.* As with mechanical systems, the energy waste in electrical systems will be determined by the condition of the electrical systems and the level of maintenance performed on them. Typical energy losses occur in loose connections, poor motor conditions, including contamination that insulates the motor, increasing its running temperature and subsequently its energy consumption.

   Improper or insufficient maintenance on mechanical drives will also increase the amount of energy required by the motor to drive the system. This, along with many other losses, will contribute to excessive energy requirements by electrical systems. As with mechanical systems, expect a 5% to 10% energy loss due to poor electrical system maintenance.

3. *Steam Systems.* Maintenance of steam-generation systems has long been recognized as having potential to produce substantial energy savings for most plants. Steam trap inspection programs, energy efficient boilers, and leak detection programs aid in reducing steam system losses.

   Depending on the amount of maintenance performed on a steam system, energy savings from 5% to as much as 15% have been reported by companies initiating better maintenance practices.

4. *Fluid Power Systems.* Fluid power systems include both hydraulic and pneumatic systems. Energy waste in these systems is generally related to leaks. Leaks can be internal or external. External leaks are easier to find, since air will make noise, and oil leaves a pool of fluid. These leaks waste energy, since the compressor or pump will have to run more frequently for the system to operate correctly. In addition, hydraulic systems will require that the spills be cleaned up, which is another form of energy waste. Internal leaks are more difficult to detect, particularly when they are small. They are usually identified by sluggish performance and, in hydraulic systems, by excessive heating of components. Again, the pumps and compressors must run more frequently to compensate for the leaks. These and

other energy losses will account for energy losses of 5% to 15% in fluid power systems.

As seen from these examples, a 5% to 10% energy reduction in the plant can be attained by a good preventive maintenance system.

Quality Cost Savings. Since Zero Breakdown Strategies address the asset/ equipment's condition, quality is impacted by poor maintenance practices. A surprising number of quality problems are eventually solved by a maintenance activity. Even if the activity is performed by the operator, the activity is one of maintaining the equipment's condition. In some companies, 60% or more of the quality problems are equipment related. In order to calculate the possible cost savings, the value of the annual production for the plant should be calculated. Next, the current first-pass quality rate should be determined. The difference between this and 100% gives the current reject rate.

The next step is to determine the reasons for the rejects. Usually a "top ten" list will account for the majority of the rejects. After examining the list, determine which causes have a maintenance solution. This is the percentage amount that can be reduced by maintenance. An estimate must be made of what percent of all the maintenance-related losses could be eliminated by a good maintenance program. This percentage multiplied by the dollar value of the company's annual production will yield the possible quality-related savings from maintenance. This number should then be added as a line item to all of the previously calculated savings.

New Capital Investment Savings. Projecting new capital equipment savings requires that you use the budget for capital equipment replacement for the current year or the projection for the next year. Once this is known, it is necessary to know the current type of maintenance activities. For example, is the company reactive or proactive in its maintenance practices? Is the company currently using good preventive and predictive techniques? The formula for calculating this savings is as follows:

NCR ($) = New capital replacement dollars budgeted
A% = The percent savings to be achieved (based on the current condition of the maintenance organization)
Currently reactive (=30%)
Preventive (=20%)
Preventive & Predictive (=10%)
Projected savings in new capital investment = NCR($) × A%.

Summary

There are many areas in a plant or facility that Zero Breakdown Strategies can impact. The first to consider is the effectiveness of current equipment management policies and practices. By eliminating waste in the use of labor and materials focused on asset/equipment maintenance, most organizations can realize significant savings. In addition, the impact of effective asset/equipment maintenance on an organization's assets is an important consideration. The more uptime that can be obtained from equipment, the more capacity the equipment can deliver. Increased capacity allows a company to be more competitive in its marketplace.

In addition, there are other areas of savings to be considered. These include energy savings, quality savings, and capital-investment savings. In reality, Zero Breakdown Strategies are endeavors that can result in millions of dollars of savings for many organizations.

Appendix A:
Troubleshooting Fundamentals

To become a good maintenance technician, it's essential to be effective at troubleshooting equipment problems. The following material is intended to serve as a general guide to mechanical troubleshooting. It does not cover all situations, but may be adapted to the majority of mechanical and fluid power equipment root cause problems.

Effective troubleshooting of mechanical equipment requires the equipment to be broken into its basic components. This appendix is divided into sections on bearings, belts, chains, and gears.

Bearings

Troubleshooting bearings requires a combination of a technician's physical senses and knowledge to identify problems. Bearing problems usually show up in the form of heat, sound, or vibration.

Heat. Heat can be discovered by merely feeling the housing in which the bearing is mounted. If the housing can be touched and isn't uncomfortable to keep your hand on it, the temperature is probably safe. If you can't keep your hand on it for more than a second, the temperature is becoming a problem, and should be investigated. If the housing is so hot it can't be touched at all, then its temperature is critical. At elevated temperatures, the grease can oxidize, the steel can change its material structure, and the bearing can expand internally and destroy the running clearance.

This method of detection may seem primitive, but many plants don't have temperature monitors installed on their bearings. If they do have monitors on the bearings, the guesswork is eliminated: the temperature can be read. At the appropriate temperature level, necessary action can be taken.

Sound and Vibration. Noisy bearings have some type of contamination problem. The contaminant is causing some form of metal-to-metal contact. Bearings that are running rough may have contamination, or may have the incorrect shaft and housing fit. The incorrect clearances cause the vibration in the bearing.

Conditions to be Checked. Any bearings that are suspect should be checked as quickly as is practical. Some of the conditions that may be checked are as follows:

1. Fatigue Failure (Fig. A-1). This type of failure has two main causes: normal wear and overload on the bearing. Normal wear means the bearing has lived its normal service life and needs to be replaced. Less than 5% of all bearings reach this point. Overload can be of two types: too much load and too much speed. The load can be a parasitic load, which is a load which doesn't belong, but is present due to some neglect on the technician's part. If the housing is too small or the shaft too large, or if a burr in the shaft or housing is present, the internal dimensions of the bearing are changed. This results in additional load placed on the bearing. While it doesn't result in immediate failure, it drastically shortens the bearing's life. Every effort must be taken to ensure that the operating conditions are as close to perfect as possible.

Figure A-1.   Fatigue. The normal failure of a bearing is fatigue. Pictured is a typical fatigue failure on an inner ring. The course-grained pattern should be noted in contrast to the pattern of a lubrication or abrasion failure. Good loading conditions are evident; the load zone arcs on both roller paths being of equal length. *(Courtesy of the Torrington Company.)*

2. Contamination (Fig. A–2). This occurs when dirt enters the bearing, causing the bearing to wear. As the wear causes the internal geometries of the bearing to change, the bearing becomes noisy and vibration begins. As time progresses, the internal clearances of the bearing are affected and the bearing won't be within tolerance and will require changing.

3. Brinelling (Fig. A–3). The blame for this problem almost always rests with the technician. It's caused by incorrectly applying force to the wrong bear-

Figure A-2. Contamination. *(Courtesy of Fafnir Bearing Div. of Textron, Inc.)*

Figure A-3. Brinelled raceway. Brinelling of the raceway illustrated was caused by roller impact. The damage occurred during mounting of the bearing. There is a displacement rather than a loss of metal in brinelling. Raceway surface brinelling results in a noisy bearing and such a mark can be the nucleus for premature failure. *(Courtesy of The Torrington Company.)*

ing race while mounting or dismounting the bearing (Fig. A–4). One rule to remember: when mounting a bearing, apply the force to the tight fit ring. This will eliminate most of the brinelling problems. Brinelling is actually a dent in the raceway caused by a force applied to the rolling element. The rolling element applies a force to the race exceeding its elastic limit, leaving the dent.

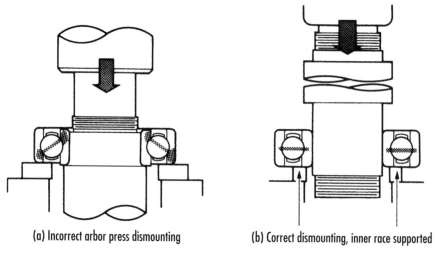

(a) Incorrect arbor press dismounting   (b) Correct dismounting, inner race supported

Figure A-4.   Incorrect versus correct method of mounting bearings: (a) force applied to wrong race, (b) force correctly applied, inner race properly supported. *(Courtesy of The Torrington Company.)*

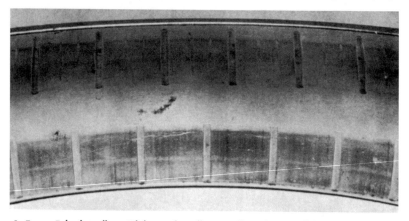

Figure A-5a.   False brinelling. While true brinelling is a flow of material due to excessive pressure that causes indentation in a part, false brinelling involves an actual removal of material and is a wear condition. The exact cause of false brinelling is not agreed upon by authorities. It is known that relative motion, load, and oxygen are prerequisites. Other names for this phenomenon are fretting corrosion and friction oxidation. *(Courtesy of The Torrington Company.)*

AXIAL VIBRATION   OSCILLATORY VIBRATION

Figure A-5a.   Vibration that causes false brinelling. *(Courtesy of Fafnir Bearing Div. of Textron, Inc.)*

4. False Brinelling (Fig. A–5a). While this failure resembles true brinelling, it's caused by an entirely different set of circumstances. Brinelling is a dent; false brinelling actually has material removed from the bearing race. Three things must be present to cause false brinelling: a stationary bearing, mounting under load, and an external vibration. The vibration under load, on the stationary bearing, causes the metal-to-metal contact. The vibration causes the ball and the race to work against each other. This wears material away from both parts (Fig. A–5b). False brinelling can be eliminated by removing any-one of the three conditions. It will not occur unless all three are present.

5. Misalignment   (Fig. A–6). This problem is usually apparent by the path the balls or rollers leave on the raceway. The best way to prevent it is to be sure that all components are properly aligned during installation. Problems as pictured in Fig. A–7 will cause rapid bearing failures.

6. Electric Arcing and Fluting (Fig. A–8). This is

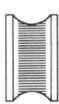
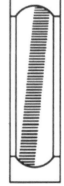

Figure A-6.   Misalignment. *(Courtesy of Fafnir Bearing Div. of Textron, Inc.)*

 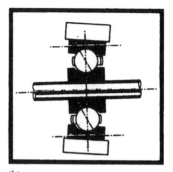

(a)
Misalignment of the shaft in relation to the housing causes an overload of the balls which will result in the failure described.

(b)
Housing misalignment may be caused either by the housings being cocked with the plane of the shaft or the housing shoulder being ground out-of-square so that it forces the outer ring to cock in relation to the inner. It may also result from settling of the frames or foundations.

Figure A-7.   (a) Shaft misalignment, (b) misalignment of the housing.

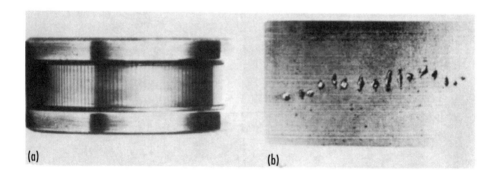

Figure A-8.   Electric arcing (a) and fluting (b). *(Courtesy of Fafnir Bearing Div. of Textron, Inc.)*

caused by electric current passing through the bearing. It may be caused by using the bearing for a path to ground while welding. It may also be caused in motors and generators by a breakdown in insulation. Some machinery develops enough static electricity to cause this form of damage. When observed, some measure must be taken to prevent current passing through the bearing or eventual premature failure will result.

Figure A-9.   Lubrication failure. *(Courtesy of Fafnir Bearing Div. of Textron, Inc.)*

7. Lubrication Failure (Fig. A-9). This type of failure is caused by one of four conditions: too much, too little, wrong type, or dirty lubricant. It's usually observed by a burnt smell and a darkened color to the lubricant. The bearing races may be discolored, and they'll be noisy. The cure is to use the right amount of the correct grade of clean lubricant.

Most bearing failures fall into these categories. If the inspection can find the bearing before it completely fails, the problem is apparent. If not, the bearing may be in such bad shape that no problem is clearly seen to be the cause. At the first sign of abnormal heat, noise, or vibration, the bearing should be inspected. Correcting the problem at the earliest possible time pays off in longer bearing life.

Belt Drives

Most belt failure information is covered in Chapter 5, Belt Drives. Included here, however, is a troubleshooting chart for quick access to the information (Table A–1).

Table A-1 Belt Failure

Problem	Possible Cause	Cure
Abrasion on the belt	Dirt in sheaves	Clean sheaves and remove source of dirt
Belts turn over in sheave	Guard rubbing belt Belts slipping in sheave Damaged tensile section Misalignment of pulleys	Adjust or replace guard Readjust tension Properly install new belts Check alignment, realign if necessary
Belt squeal	Incorrect tension	Check and adjust tension if necessary
Belt swollen and sticky	Belts overloaded Oil or grease on belt	Use higher rated belt Replace belts and eliminate source of oil or grease
Belt broken	Drive overload Foreign matter in sheave	Check drive, use higher rated belt Remove material and check guard, keep foreign matter out of sheaves
Bottom of belt cracking	Belt slipping causing hardening of the belt underside Backside idler	Check tension, adjust to avoid slippage Increase diameter of idler Use of another idler recommended
Belt whip	Insufficient tension A too-long center distance	Correct tension Increase tension, use kiss idler
Belt stretch	Broken tensile members	Properly install new belts Check for drive overloads

Table A-1 Belt Failure (continued)

Problem	Possible Cause	Cure
Rapid belt failure	Worn pulley sheaves	Check sheave for wear
	Belt damaged during installation	Properly install new belt
	Misaligned pulleys	Check and adjust alignment
	Foreign material in sheave	Remove material and improve guard
	High temperature	Ventilate guard, remove source of heat
Spin burns	Belt slipping during initial start up	Adjust tension, check belt rating
	Locked sheave	Check to ensure all components will turn
Loose belt in a multiple set	Belts mismatched	Check match code
	Old and new belts used in same set	Do not mix old and new belts, change all belts in the drive
Backing cut in a series of banded belts	Worn sheaves	Check sheaves for wear
Banded belts	Belt rubbing an obstruction	Check belt path, check guard

Chain Drives

Troubleshooting chain drives is a matter of observation. Table A–2 shows common problems with chain drives.

Table A-2 Chain Drive Problems

Problem	Possible Cause	Cure
Noisy drive	Misalignment	Check sprocket alignment
	Incorrect tension	Check slack side span for 2% deflection
	Insufficient lubrication	Check drive to ensure proper lubrication
	Worn drive	Check chain and sprocket for wear
Wear on inside of link plates and sides of sprocket teeth	Misalignment	Check drive for correct alignment
Chain climbs sprocket teeth	Chain worn	Check for chain wear
	Insufficient tension	Check chain tension
	Material in tooth pockets	Clean sprocket, eliminate cause of material buildup
Chain hangs in sprocket	Worn sprocket teeth	Check for sprocket wear
	Sticky lubricant	Use correct grade of lubricant
Stiff chain joints	Misalignment of drive	Check and correct alignment
	Worn and corroded chain	Replace chain and provide correct lubrication
Chain whip	Overloads	Reduce loads, check drive rating
	Insufficient tension	Correct the tension
	Stiff chain joints	Replace bad joints, or install new chain
	Fluctuating loads	Increase chain size, use spring-loaded idler to dampen pulsation
Broken sprocket teeth	Chain climbing sprocket	Check for chain wear, excessive slack
Drive excessively hot	Running too fast	Check drive for proper speed
	Insufficient lubrication	Check for correct lubrication
	Chain rubbing on obstruction	Check drive for obstruction, check guard design
	Wrong type of lubrication system being used	Check drive design for proper lubrication system

Gear Drives

The information on tooth failures, given in Chapter 7, is very useful in trouble-shooting gear drives. When inspecting the teeth, the photographs in that chapter should be used to identify problem areas.

The two most common areas of problems in gear drives are lubrication breakdown and misalignment. If these two areas are considered in routine maintenance, there will be very few gear breakdowns requiring troubleshooting.

Summary

Becoming an effective mechanical troubleshooter takes time and practice. The necessary skills must be developed with experience. The tables in this appendix will provide a technician with enough information to start troubleshooting.

Appendix B:
Hydraulic Troubleshooting

The following troubleshooting guides are provided as a supplement to the material presented in Chapter 11. The charts should assist in troubleshooting many common hydraulic problems.

Table B-1 Hydraulic System Problems

Problem	Possible Cause	Cure
Excessive system heat	System pressure too high	Reduce pressure to correct setting for system
	Pump not unloading during system inactivity	Check unloading valve to ensure that its setting is below that of the relief valve
	Cooler stopped up	Check for water flow
	Cooler too small	Check engineering specifications
	Reservoir too small	Check specifications
	Oil level too low	Add oil
	Internal pump leakage	Change pump
	Leakage through system components	Find the component with the hot return line indicating leakage
	Undersized piping in system	Check the original sizes to ensure no changes have been made

Table B-1 Hydraulic System Problems *(continued)*

Problem	Possible Cause	Cure
Excessive wear on system components	Incorrect viscosity oil in system	Check manufacturer's mimimum viscosity requirements
	Foreign material circulating through system	Clean the system, change all filters, add new oil
	Air in system	Stop air entry into system, usually on inlet side of pump
Noisy pump	Cavitation	Check inlet pressure, ensure that there are no inlet restrictions
	Air leak on inlet side	Be sure all fittings are tight
	Misalignment	Check coupling alignment
	Low oil level	Fill to proper level to prevent the pump from drawing in air

Table B-2 Directional Control Valve (DCV) Problems

Problem	Possible Cause	Cure
Valve sluggish	Dirt in system	Clean valve, clean fluid in system, change filters
	Internal drain blocked	Clear drain, clear line
	Mounting bolts too tight	Torque valve body bolts according to manufacturer's instruction
	Grounded solenoid coil	Check for ground, repair or replace coils
Valve fails to shift	Dirt in system	Clean valve, fluid, filters
	Blocked internal drain	Clean drain lines
	No pilot pressure	Check for source of pressure loss
	Solenoid voltage absent	Find location of voltage drop
	Mounting bolts too tight	Torque to correct specification
Valve actuation products unusual response	Lines reversed	Check for proper connection
	Internal components installed incorrectly	Check prints to ensure proper assembly

Table B-3 Hydraulic Motor Problems

Problem	Possible Cause	Cure
Motor running in reverse direction	Lines crossed at motor Lines reversed at DCV	Reverse lines Reverse lines
Motor will not come up to speed, has no torque	Insufficient system pressure	Check system, relief valve, pump, etc.
External oil leakage	Internal motor leakage Drain line stopped up Seals and packing leaking	Repair or replace motor Clean line Repair or replace seals, packing
Motor will not turn over	Insufficient pressure for given load	Check load and system pressure

Table B-4 Hydraulic Cylinder Problems

Problem	Possible Cause	Cure
Will not extend or retract	Insufficient flow or pressure	Check system for proper flow and pressure
	Too-heavy load	Check load rating of equipment
	Mechanical bind	Check alignment of system, cylinder to load
	Internal leakage of cylinder	Repair or replace cylinder Check by monitoring flow in return line; if there is flow, the cylinder is leaking through
Erratic action	Air in system	Bleed air from lines, find the leak and repair
	Internal leakage	Check to ensure leakage, then repair or replace cylinder
	Cylinder binding	Misalignment, align cylinder Worn cylinder parts, repair or replace cylinder components

Appendix C:
Pneumatic Troubleshooting

As in hydraulic systems, pneumatic troubleshooting involves knowledge of system components. This knowledge will make the use of the following tables easier when troubleshooting pneumatic systems. Table C–1 should be used as a guide for pneumatic troubleshooting.

Table C-1 Pneumatic System Problems

Problem	Possible Cause	Cure
Low air pressure	Compressor volumetric output insufficient	Install a second compressor or a receiver in system
	Leaks in system	Repair all leaks
	Air filters are dirty	Clean or replace filters
	Internal compressor components worn	Repair or replace defective parts
Noisy operation	Defective components in compressor	Repair or replace defective part
	Inadequate lubrication	Increase lubrication
	Misalignment	Align correctly
Air temperature high between stages	Intercooler stopped up	Clean and flush intercooler
	Water temperature too hot	Cool water before entering intercooler

Table C-1 Pneumatic System Problems *(continued)*

Problem	Possible Cause	Cure
Insufficient air volume in system	Plugged inlet filter Worn compressor component	Change or clean inlet filter Repair or replace worn parts
Oil in air lines	Worn compressor rings Defective lubricator	Replace compressor rings Check flow rate of lubricator for proper amount
Water in system	Defective oil separator Inlet bringing in moist air Cooler not working Moisture separator not working	Clean, drain, repair separator Reposition inlet Repair coolers; drain, clean also to help with moisture removal Service separator

Glossary

Abrasive: A substance that wears or grinds away by friction.

Absolute: A pressure scale where a vacuum is 0 psi and atmospheric pressure is 14.7 psi.

Acceleration: The rate of change of an object's velocity.

Addendum: The distance from the pitch line to the tip of the tooth in a gear.

Additive: A substance added to a lubricant to improve or enhance a quality.

Alignment: The proper positioning of two components in relation to one another.

Backlash: The amount of clearance between two gear teeth in mesh.

Bevel: A gear with teeth that are cut into the face of the gear. The gears may intersect at almost any angle.

Bleeding: The process of an oil working out of the base in a grease.

Bolt: A fastening device used with a nut to hold two or more parts together. The bolt is tightened by turning the nut.

Bushing: A cylindrical device used to reduce the friction between two moving parts.

Cavitation: A process in which dissolved air is removed from the fluid on the inlet side of the pump and implodes back into the fluid on the outlet side of the pump.

Chordal thickness: The thickness of a gear tooth measured on the pitch line. A straight line measurement.

Circular thickness: The thickness of a gear tooth measured on the pitch circle. This measurement is an arc. Usually only given on spur gears.

Clearance: The radial distance between the tip of a gear tooth and the bottom of the mating tooth space.

Compression Packing: Packing that accomplishes sealing by being deformed under pressure.

Corrosion: A process where material is worn away gradually, usually by some form of a chemical action.

Coupling: Device used to connect shafting.

Cylinder: A fluid power component that is used for linear motion. Sometimes called a linear actuator.

Deceleration: The process of reducing an object's velocity.

Dedendum: The distance from the pitch circle to the root of a tooth.

Density: The mass of a material for a given volume.

Depth of engagement: The radial engagement of a screw thread.

Dropping point: The temperature at which a grease liquifies.

Dynamic: A type of friction relating to objects in motion.

Efficiency: A ratio of the input energy to the output energy. Usually expressed as a percentage.

End-play: Motion along the axis of a shaft.

Fit: A designation used to indicate the closeness of two mating screw threads.

Flash point: The temperature at which a substance will burst into flames.

Friction: The resistance to motion of two bodies in contact. The three types are: static, dynamic, and rolling.

Gauge: A pressure scale. This scale ignores atmospheric pressure. Atmospheric pressure is 0 psig.

Gear: A mechanical toothed wheel that provides a drive with a positive transmission of torque.

Helical: A form of gear tooth that's cut at a helix angle on the face of the gear.

Herringbone: A gear with two sets of teeth with opposite hands cut into the face. The helix angles of both sets of teeth are the same.

Hub: The center part of a coupling or sprocket.

Humidity: The measure of the amount of water vapor in a given volume of air.

Hydrodynamic: A physical property by which a rotating body can develop pressure in a surrounding fluid. Some bearings depend on this principle to support their load.

Hydrostatic: A type of bearing that has fluid pressure supplied to it by an external source.

Hypoid bevel: A bevel gear that has an offset axis. The shafts may be extended to provide more support for the gear.

Input: Power or speed put into some mechanical or fluid power component.

Interference: A form of wear in a gear drive where the two gears are in tooth tip-to-root contact.

Internal gear: A gear with the teeth cut on the inside circumference of the pitch circle.

Keyway: A groove or channel cut into a mechanical component for a key.

Lantern ring: A ring in a stuffing box used to provide lubrication for the packing.

Lead: The amount of axial distance traveled by the turning of the threaded component one turn.

Length of engagement: The axial length that two threaded components are in contact.

Lubricant: A substance introduced between two or more moving components to reduce friction and wear.

Major diameter: The outside diameter of a screw thread, measured radially.

Mass: The measure of the amount of material in an object.

Mesh: The size of one of the openings in a filter or strainer. *Also*: The working contact of gear teeth.

Micron: A unit of measure equal to 0.000039 inch.

Minor diameter: The smallest diameter of a screw thread measured radially at the root of the thread.

Motor: Hydraulic device for converting flow to rotary motion. May also be a prime mover in a mechanical or fluid power system electric motor.

Multiple threads: More than one set of threads progressing along the axial length of a threaded device.

Nominal: A term in rating a filter that refers to its approximate size in microns.

Nonpositive displacement: A condition in a pump or compressor that does not produce a given volume per revolution.

Number of threads: The number of threads per inch of axial length on a screw thread.

Orifice: A restriction to flow in a fluid power system.

Output: The power or speed delivered by a mechanical or fluid power drive.

Oxidation: The process of a material combining with oxygen; usually results in the formation of rust.

Penetration: A test to check the thickness of a grease, done by dropping a fixed weight (cone shaped) into the grease from a given height. The depth the cone penetrates is the grease's penetration rating.

Pin: A type of chain link used to connect two roller links.

Pinion: The smaller of two gears in a gear drive.

Pitch: The distance from a point on a gear to the corresponding point on the next tooth. In a chain drive, it's the distance from a point on one chain link to the corresponding point on the next link.

Pitch diameter: The diameter of an imaginary circle that connects all the pitch points on a gear or sprocket.

Planetary: A type of internal gear drive having several internal gears rotating around a center "sun" gear.

Pneumatics: A field of power transmission that uses a gas for the transmitting medium.

Positive displacement: A condition in a pump or compressor that displaces a certain volume for every revolution.

Power: A force moving through a distance in a given time period.

Pressure: Force per unit of area.

Pumpability: The ability of a lubricant to be pumped.

Rack and pinion: A type of gear drive that translates rotary motion to linear motion or vice versa.

Radial: A type of load on a bearing that is applied 90° to the shaft axis.

Relative humidity: The ratio of the amount of water vapor that a given volume of air contains compared to the amount of water vapor that it could contain. Usually expressed as a percentage.

Roller: A type of chain link composed of a bushing, link plate, and a roller.

Root: In a gear drive, the bottom area between two teeth. In a screw thread, it's the lowest point between two threads.

Runout: A movement along the axis of an object, usually a shaft.

Screw: A simple machine that utilizes the principle of the inclined plane by wrapping the inclined plane around a cylinder.

Seal cage: Same as lantern ring; a device used to lubricate the packing in a stuffing box.

Spiral bevel: A bevel gear that has the teeth cut in a spiral form on the face of the gear.

Sprocket: A wheel that has teeth cut into its outside circumference for engagement with a chain.

Spur: A gear tooth form where the teeth are cut parallel to the shaft axis.

Static: A type of friction between two surfaces in direct contact but not in motion.

Stud: A fastening device threaded on each end.

Stuffing box: An assembly that uses packing to seal an area of low pressure from an area of high pressure.

Thrust: A type of load that's applied along a shaft axis.

Torque: A force applied at a distance that attempts to produce rotation. It doesn't have to produce motion to produce torque.

Velocity: The rate of motion in a given direction.

Viscosity: The measure of the fluid's resistance to flow.

Volume: The measure of the space an object occupies, measured in cubic units.

Weight: The measure of the gravitational attraction of the earth for an object. ·

Whole depth: In a gear drive, the radial measure of a tooth space.

Work: A force times the distance it moves. Motion must occur for work to take place.

Working depth: The sum of the addendums of two mating gears.

Worm: A type of gear drive for use at right angles. It uses a screw-shaped worm with a mating gear.

Zerol bevel: A bevel gear that uses spiral shaped teeth with a zero spiral angle.

A

absolute humidity, 156
absorption dryer, 160
accumulator, 148
actuator, 164
aftercooler, 158
air spinning bearings, 56
Allen socket screw, 38
angular contact bearings, 48
animal oils, 28
annular gear, 96
asset baseline, 190
asset cost, 196
asset utilization, 1
automatic lubrication, 30

B

babbitt, 43
backlash, 100
backlog, 14–15
ball bearings, 46
bath lubrication, 26
bearing cleanliness, 55
bearing failure, 53
bearing maintenance, 53
bearing preload, 49
bearing seals, 54
bearing shield, 55
belt codes, 70, 79
belt creep, 62
belt dressing, 73
belt drives, 61
belt guards, 70
belt idlers, 70
belt sizes, 64–66, 70
belt slip, 62
belt tension, 61, 70
bevel gear, 98–99
bolt grades, 36
bolt, 35
braid over braid packing, 121
breakdowns, 3–5
bronze, 43
button head socket screw, 39

C

canvas belts, 63
capacity losses, 3
carbon graphite, 43
cavitation, 138
check valve, 149
chemical dryer, 160
CMMS
    (see computerized maintenance
    management system)
computerized maintenance
    management system, 7, 8, 19–22
conrad bearings, 46
construction standards, 176
corrective maintenance, 9
cost justification, 196
coupling alignment, 116
coupling installation, 113–116
coupling keys, 114
coupling lubrication, 115
couplings, 111
craft technician training programs, 17
cross training, 18
cross-trained environment, 18
cup packing, 127
cylindrical roller bearings, 51

D

deep groove ball bearings, 46
density, 132–133
depth of engagement, 35
dew point, 156
directional control valve, 149–150, 163
downtime cost, 197
drip lubrication, 25

E

EAM
    (see enterprise asset management)
energy cost saving, 198
energy maximization, 11
enterprise asset management, 8, 14, 19
equipment availability, 2
equipment baselines, 190